# VOLUME 6

Gosho Aoyama

# Case Briefing:

Subject: Jimmy Kudo a.k.a. Conan Edogawa
Occupation: High School Student/Detective
Special Skills: Analytical thinking and deductive reasoning, Soccer
Equipment: Bow Tie Voice Transmitter, Super Sneakers, Homing Glasses, Stretchy Suspenders

The subject is hot on the trail of a pair of suspicious men in black when he is attacked from behind and is administered a strange substance, which physically transforms him into a first grader. When the subject confides in the eccentric inventor Dr. Agasa, they decide to keep the subject's true identity a secret for the safety of everyone around him. Assuming the new identity of first-grader Conan Edogawa, the subject continues to assist the police force on their most baffling cases. The only problem is that most crime-solving professionals don't want to listen to a little kid.

One day, a woman falsely claiming to be Conan's mother appears along with a mysterious masked man. Could they be from the same organization as the men in black? Will Conan be able to outwit this nefarious duo?

# Table of Contents

# CASE CLOSED Vol. 6
## Gollancz Manga Edition

### STORY AND ART BY
### GOSHO AOYAMA

**English Adaptation**
**Naoko Amemiya**

**Translation**
**Joe Yamazaki**

**Touch-Up & Lettering**
**Walden Wong**

**Cover Design**
**Veronica Casson**

**Interior Graphics & Layout Design**
**Andrea Rice**

**Editor**
**Andy Nakatani**

**UK Cover Adaptation**
**Sue Michniewicz**

© 1994 Gosho AOYAMA/Shogakukan Inc.
First published by Shogakukan Inc. in Japan as "Meitantei Conan."
English publication rights in United Kingdom arranged by Shogakukan Inc.
through VIZ Media, LLC, U.S.A., Tuttle-Mori Agency, Inc., Japan and Ed Victor Ltd., U.K.
New and adapted artwork and text © 2005 VIZ Media, LLC. All rights reserved.
This edition published in Great Britain in 2005 by Gollancz Manga,
an imprint of the Orion Publishing Group, Orion House, 5 Upper St Martin's Lane,
London WC2H 9EA, and a licensee of VIZ Media, LLC.

1  3  5  7  9  10  8  6  4  2

The right of Gosho Aoyama to be identified as the author of this work has been asserted by
him in accordance with the  Copyright, Designs and Patents Act 1988.

A CIP catalogue record for this book is available from the British Library

ISBN 0 575 07821 9

Printed and bound at
Mackays of Chatham, PLC

www.orionbooks.co.uk

# FILE·1:
# THE TRUTH UNDER THE MASK

DARN IT !!!

NO!

*TP*
*TP*
*TP*

I'M TRAPPED !!!

*TP*
*TP*

THAT MASKED MAN WILL KILL ME!!!

BUT IF THEY CATCH ME, I'M AS GOOD AS DEAD.

SHOOT! I FINALLY FOUND SOME COHORTS OF THOSE GUYS IN BLACK THAT MADE ME SHRINK!

WHAT SHOULD I DO !?

WHAT SHOULD I DO !?

WHAT SHOULD I DO ?

TP

TP

THESE HOTEL DOORS LOCK AUTOMATICALLY SO ALL YOU HAVE TO DO IS CLOSE THE DOOR, OKAY?

OKAY!

LISTEN, MASAO.

KCHAK

!?

PTNK

CLICK

CREAK

TP

TP

WHAT TOOK YOU SO LONG ?

I'LL BE BACK SOON!

BYE, MOMMY!

TP

TP

A B-BUR-GLAR...!

HI THERE! HEH HEH.

HUF

HUF

HUF

I'M FROM PLANET RAMPO. I'M CHASING AN EVIL SPACE ALIEN WHO HAS COME TO YOUR PLANET.

SHHH. DO NOT BE AFRAID.

...

I AM SPACE DETECTIVE CONAN !!!

AGH! WAIT!

JUST YOU WAIT! I'M GONNA CALL THE POLICE!

CLICK

I, UH, I CAN'T.

THEN LEMME SEE WHAT YOU REALLY LOOK LIKE!

SEE! YOU ARE A BURGLAR !!

I'M J-JUST DISGUISED AS A KID TO FOOL MY TARGET.

NO WAY! YOU'RE JUST A KID!

8

STOP IT, MASAO! THAT'S ENOUGH!!!

I FOOLED HIM WITH THE VOICE MODULATOR.

HA HA HA...

WOW! AWESOME! YOU REALLY ARE A SPACE DETECTIVE!!

HEH HEH... I'M FROM PLANET RAMPO! I CAN TALK USING ANY VOICE I WANT!!

M-MOMMY'S VOICE...!

BESIDES, I WANT TO GET MY HANDS ON THE MASKED MAN'S PILLS-- THE ONES THAT MADE ME SHRINK!

IF I CAN'T SNEAK INTO THEIR ROOM QUICKLY, THAT BIG MAN THEY'RE TALKING TO WILL DIE.

BUT WHAT DO I DO NOW?

OKAY. BUT WHAT'S THE GUM FOR?

HEH HEH... IT'S FOR SUPER-DUPER TOP SECRET SPACE DETECTIVE STUFF!!

HUH? THIS?

...AND THE GUM YOU HAVE.

LET'S SEE. FOR NOW I NEED THAT PHONE...

I WANNA HELP, TOO! CAN I? CAN I?

GLANCE

301

KNOCK
KNOCK

RATTLE
RATTLE

WHAT
?

30

KCHAK

ROOM
SERVICE--
YOUR FOOD
AND WINE.

WHAT?
WE DIDN'T
ORDER
ANYTHING
LIKE
THAT!!

B-BUT
...

I COULD
USE A
BITE TO
EAT. HAVE
HIM BRING
IT IN.

WHAT'S
THE
HARM
?

HEH
...

THAT'S
STRANGE
...

.....

BUT
SOMEONE
JUST CALLED
US AND
REQUESTED
THIS
DELIVERY
TO YOUR
ROOM.

FWISH

!?

GUM INSIDE THE LOCK !?

...

HEH HEH HEH ...

SHALL WE TOAST ?

TP
TP

CLANK

PTNK

CLICK

12

FIRST LET ME INTRODUCE OUR OTHER GUEST.

WAIT...

IS IT THAT BOY!?

IS SOMEBODY UNDER THERE!?

GUEST?

OTHER GUEST...?

HEH HEH HEH. THAT CART IS A DECOY.

NO-BODY'S HERE!

!?

ZHOOP

...INSIDE...

GRAB

HE IS ACTUALLY...

... THE CLOSET!!

BAM

THEN WHILE OUR ATTENTION WAS ON THE CART, YOU SLIPPED INTO THE ROOM AND HID IN THE CLOSET!!

HEH HEH HEH. WHILE WE WERE TALKING TO THE BELLHOP YOU SUMMONED, YOU SHOVED GUM INTO THE LOCK TO DISABLE IT.

DAMN IT!!!

AGH!

DAMN. I'LL HAVE TO USE THE WRIST WATCH TRANQUILIZER GUN TO--

HEH HEH. DID YOU REALLY THINK I'D FALL FOR THAT?

FWAP

? HA HA HA HA !!

HEH HEH...

HUH?

IT'S A T-TOY?

PLIK

BWAH HAH!

BOINGA BOING

THE WORLD'S PRE-EMINENT MYSTERY NOVELIST...

SHFF

YOU STILL CAN'T TELL? IT'S ME! IT'S ME!

...BOOKER KUDO !!!

HA HA...

TUG

THEN THAT WOMAN... IS SHE...?

DAD!

D-DA--

I'M SORRY, JIMMY DEAR.

RIP

MOM!!!

FSHA

GRIN

I SEE. YOU GUYS DID ALL THIS TO SET ME UP.

DOC AGASA!!

SHFF

HA HA HA

THEN THAT MEANS THAT BIG MAN IS...

SO I FOOLED MY OWN CHILD! JUST GOES TO SHOW I CAN STILL CUT IT AS AN ACTRESS. ♡

THONK

**SULK**

IT'S NOT A SINISTER PLOT!

WE WERE TESTING YOUR ABILITIES AS A DETECTIVE.

HA HA. SO YOU HEARD FROM DOC AGASA HOW I BECAME SMALL AND YOU COOKED UP THIS SINISTER PLOT.

THAT'S RIGHT, JIMMY. WE CAME HOME AFTER A LONG ABSENCE ONLY TO FIND YOU WEREN'T THERE.

C'MON, DON'T BE SO MAD. WE WERE WORRIED ABOUT YOU.

IT'S JUST AS I PLANNED!

YOU EVEN MANAGED TO SNEAK IN HERE, BUT I FOUND YOU AND SHOT YOU!

YOU MADE A BRILLIANT ESCAPE AND THEN TRACKED US HERE FROM THE CLUES I LEFT BEHIND.

I THOUGHT I WAS GONNA BE KILLED!

YEAH? GOOD, GOOD!

I WENT TO THE TROUBLE OF DRESSING UP AS THE PHANTOM NIGHT BARON CHARACTER FROM MY NOVEL, TOO!

IT'S YOUR OWN FAULT FOR NOT REALIZING THE TRUTH!

ARE YOU CRAZY!? I HAD MY HANDS FULL!

OF COURSE! I'D SAY YOU BARELY PASS MUSTER AS A DETECTIVE.

THEN YOU KNEW I WAS HIDING IN THAT KITCHEN STORAGE SPACE, DIDN'T YOU!?

HUH?

COME LIVE A LIFE OF PEACE WITH US OVER-SEAS!!

THEN LET'S LEAVE THIS DANGEROUS COUNTRY.

...YOU'D BE DEAD BY NOW.

IF WE'D BEEN THE BAD GUYS...

BANG

THAT'S WHY I AGREED TO BE A PART OF THIS ACT, JIMMY.

......

THAT'S RIGHT, JIMMY. WE ACTUALLY DID ALL OF THIS TO SHOW YOU HOW MUCH DANGER YOU'RE IN!

NO WAY!

SO STOP PLAYING DETECTIVE. IT'S TOO DANGEROUS.

...

I'LL ASK THEM TO LOOK INTO THIS CRIME SYNDICATE.

WE'LL GET SOME OF THAT POISON SOON ENOUGH, AND YOU'LL BE BACK TO NORMAL.

BUT DON'T WORRY, I HAVE FRIENDS IN INTERPOL.

JIMMY! OH...

YOU TWO JUST STAY OUT OF IT!!

THIS IS *MY* CASE AND I INTEND TO SOLVE IT!!

... I NEED TO STAY IN JAPAN!!

BESIDES... I...

HMPH. OH WELL... LET HIM HAVE HIS WAY FOR A WHILE.

JIMMY!!

...

...

IT SEEMS TO ME THERE MIGHT BE ANOTHER REASON JIMMY DOESN'T WANT TO LEAVE. HM?

BUT, HONEY...

BUT THE MOMENT THINGS GET DANGEROUS, WE'RE TAKING YOU OUT OF THE COUNTRY!!

BUT MA'AM--

YES... HE SAYS THIS IS WHERE HE REALLY WANTS TO BE.

WHAT! YOU'RE LEAVING YOUR SON WITH US AGAIN!?

WOW! ¥10 MILLION!

PLEASE FEEL FREE TO USE AS MUCH AS YOU NEED.

HUH?

THIS IS FOR HIS EX-PENSES!

PLEASE TAKE GOOD CARE OF HIM!

Y-YES ...?

OH, AND MISS RACHEL?

HO HO HO ...

IT'LL BE A PLEASURE TO TAKE CARE OF YOUR DARLING BOY!!

HA HA HA HA HA

OH, THANK YOU!

MY BOY SEEMS TO LIKE YOU VERY MUCH!

OH, HE'LL GIVE UP AND COME CRYING TO US SOON ENOUGH!

BUT WILL JIMMY BE ALL RIGHT?

WELL THAT WAS A LOT OF FUN! IT WAS WORTH DITCHING MY MANUSCRIPTS TO COME TO JAPAN!

--NARITA AIRPORT--

WHOOOSH

THERE HE IS!

OOH! SOUNDS NICE! ♡

SO HOW 'BOUT WE TAKE A ROUND-THE-WORLD-TRIP RIGHT NOW?

HEY HEY! WE'VE GOT OUR PRESSES ON HOLD!!

WE GOT A CALL FROM YOUR SON! NOW GET TO WORK WRITING THE REMAINING 308 PAGES YOU OWE US!!

NO WAY. WE'RE FIRST!!

HOW'D YOU KNOW WHERE I WAS!?

TH-THE GUYS FROM THE FOREIGN MAGAZINES!!

MR. KUDO!!

THUDDA THUDDA

YAAAWN.

THAT ROTTEN KID.

HE GOT YOU.

KLAKKETA KLAK

# FILE 2: THREE VISITORS?

23

I'M ABSOLUTELY CERTAIN.

I-I KNEW IT.

YOUR WIFE IS INDEED HAVING AN AFFAIR.

PLEASE TAKE A GOOD LOOK AROUND HER EYES.

FLICK

!?

SHE MANAGED TO CONCEAL HER FACE WITH THE GLASSES AND A HAT, BUT SHE COULDN'T HIDE THAT MOLE BY HER EYE.

BUT IS THIS WOMAN REALLY MY WIFE INEKO?

DENJIRO MARU (AGE 51) PRESIDENT OF THE MARU GROUP

.....

YES, THAT IS INEKO MARU!!

I'VE NO DOUBT THAT SHE IS INDEED YOUR WIFE.

KATONK

...BUT THEN WE HAVE TO STOP BY HERE!

FOR ONCE HE TAKES US OUT TO EAT...

HOW LONG IS THE OLD MAN GONNA MAKE US WAIT?

LOOK! IT JUMPED AGAIN!

SPLISH

I MEAN, REALLY! WHAT KIND OF DETECTIVE BRINGS A KID ALONG WHEN HE'S REPORTING ON AN ADULTERY CASE?

25

CREEEAK

MM?

CREAK

A VISITOR?

TMP TMP

TMP

OH... THAT'S RIGHT. I HAVE APPOINTMENTS WITH TWO OR THREE OTHER PEOPLE TODAY.

HMM. A VISITOR?

DING DONG

WELL? WHO IS HE?

YES.

AH... I DON'T KNOW YET.

M-MY WIFE IS WITH THIS MAN THREE TIMES A WEEK?

NO... INEKO LEFT BEFORE NOON SAYING SHE HAD A KOTO LESSON.

OH YEAH... SINCE YOU WERE COMING, I TOLD THEM TO TAKE A BREAK AND GO OUT FOR A WHILE.

YOUR WIFE TOO?

HEY, ISN'T ANYBODY GONNA GET THAT!?

DING DONG DING DONG

DAMN IT! WHAT GOOD IS THE HELP FOR!

... I CAN'T EVEN BE SURE OF THAT.

BUT NOW THAT I'VE SEEN THIS...

DAMN THAT INEKO.

STOMP STOMP

I'LL BE RIGHT BACK. PLEASE WAIT HERE!

I'M GOING TO SHOW THE VISITOR IN TO THE ANNEX!

ZHOOP

CHAK

EVERY- BODY'S OUT JUST NOW.

RATTLE

I'M SORRY TO KEEP YOU WAITING.

BRRRRING...

HE PROBABLY CAN'T HEAR IT FROM THE ANNEX.

BRRRING...

BRRRING...

BRRRING...

ZHOOD

DAMN IT! WHERE THE HELL'S THE OLD MAN!?

BRRRING...

BRRRING...

BRRRING...

BRRRING...

BRRRING...

BRRRING...

BRRRING...

BRRRING...

BRRRING...

BRRRING...

BRRRING...

...

DAMN!!

SLAM!

HEY, IT STOPPED.

BRRR...

!?

IT WAS KIND OF CREEPY SOUNDING.

LIKE SOMETHING BEING HIT... OR SCRATCHED.

HUH? NO.

LIKE WHAT?

DID YOU HEAR A STRANGE SOUND JUST NOW?

IT CAME FROM THE ANNEX.

D-DON'T SCARE ME LIKE THAT!!

TICK TICK

TICK

...

REALLY!

CAW CAW

BRRRING...

YEAH. HE DID SAY HE'D BE RIGHT BACK.

DON'T YOU THINK THE MAN'S BEEN AWAY FOR TOO LONG?

IT STOPPED. THIS TIME IT RANG THREE TIMES.

BRRR...

ZHOOP

AGH! DAMN IT!!

IT'S THE PHONE AGAIN.

BRRRING...

BRRRING...

BRRRING...

ZHOOP

THE NERVE !

HE'S MADE ME WAIT FOR TWO HOURS ALREADY! WHAT'S THAT OLD MAN THINKING?

30

D-DAD!!

THAT'S IT. I'VE HAD IT!! I'M GOING TO THE ANNEX!!

TMP TMP

WHAT'S GOING ON?

THREE TIMES AGAIN.

BRRRING...

BRRRING...

BRR...

...

WHAT'S WRONG!?

WHAT IS IT!?

BAM

DASH

AGH!

AAAAAAAAGH!

!?

WE JUST BUMPED INTO MRS. MARU OUTSIDE.

WE'RE THE MAIDS HERE!

WHO ARE YOU PEOPLE?

OH...

WHAT IS THIS COMMOTION?

WHO ARE YOU PEOPLE?

HEY!

HEY! I'M JUST THE DETECTIVE MR. MARU HIRED!!

MY!

IDIOT!

WHEN WE RETURNED HOME, THIS STRANGER WAS ROAMING AROUND INSIDE!!

MA'AM!

INEKO MARU (34) DENJIRO MARU'S WIFE

WHAT BUSINESS WOULD A DETECTIVE HAVE HERE?

ER...

DETECTIVE...?

Y-YES MA'AM!!

MS. KUMI? MS. SAORI? PLEASE GO GET MY HUSBAND!!

THAT'S JUST IT. HE WENT OVER TO THE ANNEX AND HASN'T COME BACK.

AND WHERE IS MY HUSBAND?

Y-YOU'LL HAVE TO ASK YOUR HUSBAND DIRECTLY.

B-BUT, MA'AM.

SO PLEASE LIE ABOUT THE AFFAIR TO MY HUSBAND.

I'LL PAY YOU DOUBLE WHAT HE PAID!!

HUH?

HOW MUCH DO YOU KNOW?

SO...

TA TA TA

RACHEL
!!

CALL
THE
POLICE
!!!

WHAT
THE--!?

THE
POLICE
...

CLICK CLICK CLICK

THE VICTIM IS DENJIRO MARU, 51 YEARS OLD.

CAUSE OF DEATH IS MOST LIKELY THE SWORD STABBED IN HIS CHEST.

WHEEOO WHEEOO WHEEOO

...TO MR. MARU'S DEATH.

...THE VICTIM AND THE PERPETRATOR MUST HAVE FOUGHT...

JUDGING FROM THE RANSACKED ROOM AND THE NUMEROUS LACERATIONS ON THE BODY...

THAT MEANS THE SUSPECT MUST ALSO BE A MASTER SWORDS-MAN.

HMM... SO HE'S QUITE SKILLED.

MY HUSBAND'S HOBBY WAS THE IAI SWORD DRAWING TECHNIQUE. I BELIEVE HE'S RANKED WITH A THIRD DEGREE.

MY HUSBAND DISPLAYED THAT SWORD IN THE ALCOVE FOR DECORATION!

BUT WHY IS THE SWORD HERE?

IS THAT TRUE?

*I* SAW SOMEONE VISIT-- SOMEONE THAT COULD'VE BEEN THE SUSPECT!

NO, INSPECTOR. THE VICTIM HAD INSTRUCTED ME TO WAIT FOR HIM BACK IN THE OTHER BUILDING, SO *ER...*

SO, RICHARD, AS USUAL YOU JUST HAPPEN TO BE AT THE SCENE OF A CRIME, *HUH*? SEE ANY SUSPICIOUS CHARACTERS?

...I BET HE WAS THE MURDERER AND THAT HE SNUCK OUT THE BACK GATE AFTER KILLING HIM HERE!

THE BACK GATE NEAR THE ANNEX WAS OPEN, SO...

*YEAH!* THE VISITOR AND THE DEAD MAN WENT INTO THIS ANNEX AND NEVER CAME OUT.

INSPECTOR! WE FOUND THIS DATE BOOK IN THE VICTIM'S POCKET!

AND HE'S A MASTER SWORDS-MAN.

*HMM.* SO IT'S LIKELY THAT THE PERPE-TRATOR HAD AN APPOINT-MENT WITH THE VICTIM.

AND SO? DID YOU SEE THE PERPE-TRATOR'S FACE?

TH-THE KID AGAIN.

NOPE. I WAS NEAR THE POND AND THE BUSHES BLOCKED MY VIEW. I ONLY SAW HIS LEGS.

LET'S SEE. TODAY HE WAS SCHEDULED TO MEET ...

*FLIP*

*MM?* IT'S PACKED WITH APPOINT-MENTS.

(Wed)

7

(Thur)

8 (Fri)

9 (Sat)

PM 2:00 Meeting with management

Richard Moore Yuji Suwa
Ikuya Hatano Makoto Akutsu

PM 7:00~9:

... THESE FOUR !!

WHY, IF IT ISN'T ...

N-NO, I'M ...

WHAT !?

INSPECTOR!! THIS MAN WAS LOITERING IN FRONT OF THE HOUSE!!

COME TO THINK OF IT, THE OLD MAN SAID HE WAS MEETING TWO OR THREE MORE PEOPLE BESIDES ME.

THEN THIS "IKUYA HATANO" IN THE DATE BOOK IS YOU?

TH-THAT IS MY NAME.

HE IS MY HUSBAND'S PHYSICIAN! MY HUSBAND WAS A DIABETIC. WE HAVE DOCTOR HATANO COME ONCE A WEEK TO GIVE HIM A CHECKUP!

... DOCTOR HATANO !!

WHO DO YOU THINK I AM!?

WHAT THE HELL !?

MM !?

YEAH!! I CAME TO SEE THE MASTER HERE!

AKUTSU? MAKOTO AKUTSU?

I'M THE GREAT SCULPTOR AKUTSU!!

OH, I GOT IT!!

!!

MM... SO NOW WE HAVE THREE OUT OF THE FOUR PEOPLE WRITTEN IN THE DATE BOOK.

HUH?

WHAT IS THIS COMMOTION ABOUT?

THAT MEANS THIS YUJI SUWA MUST BE THE MURDERER.

THERE'S ONLY ONE PERSON WHO'S NOT HERE.

THE MURDERER HAS ALREADY BEEN HERE TO SEE THE VICTIM.

!?

?

OH. SO YOU CAME.

I AM.

Y-YOU'RE NOT... YUJI SUWA, ARE YOU?

D-DON'T PAY HIM ANY ATTENTION!!

......

SCAT

WHO IS THIS BOY?

STARE

C-CONAN!

MM?

HEY, MISTER?

WHAT?

YOU'RE AN IAI SWORDSMAN, AREN'T YOU?

YOU'RE AN IAI SWORDSMAN, AREN'T YOU?

WHAT?

IT'S RIGHT BETWEEN YOUR THUMB AND YOUR INDEX FINGER!

SEE THAT NARROW SCAR?

YOUR LEFT HAND!

HOW DID YOU KNOW, BOY?

WHEN YOU SHEATH THE SWORD, YOU HOLD THE OPEN END OF THE SHEATH WITH YOUR THUMB AND INDEX FINGER!

IAI PRACTIONERS SOMETIMES GET CUTS THERE WHEN THEY PUT THE SWORD BACK INTO THE SHEATH!

THE MASTER OF THIS HOUSE, MR. DENJIRO, ATTENDED MY DOJO. I CAME TODAY TO REPAY HIM THE MONEY I HAD BORROWED.

HMM...

Y-YES... THIS IS AN OLD SCAR I GOT BACK WHEN I WAS INEXPERIENCED.

NOW I'M FINALLY GOOD ENOUGH TO HAVE MY OWN DOJO.

I-IS THAT TRUE?

THAT'S WHY I THOUGHT YOU MIGHT DO IAI.

HMM?

I SEE... YOU COULDN'T PAY BACK WHAT YOU OWED SO INSTEAD YOU DID HIM IN, HUH?

WHAT?

HE WAS MURDERED.

HEY HEY! WHAT'CHA TALKING 'BOUT?

HEH! DON'T PLAY DUMB.

"DID HIM IN"?

DID SOMETHING HAPPEN TO MR. MARU?

INSIDE THE ANNEX!!

!?

WHO WOULD DO SUCH A THING?

WH-WHO...?

M-MR. DENJIRO...!

HE WAS DISCOVERED APPROXIMATELY TWO HOURS LATER WHEN THE HOUSEMAIDS RETURNED.

...SOMEBODY CAME TO VISIT THE VICTIM, MR. DENJIRO MARU, AROUND 3 P.M. THEY BOTH ENTERED THIS ANNEX.

RICHARD, RACHEL AND CONAN WERE ON THE ESTATE AT THE TIME OF THE CRIME. ACCORDING TO THEIR TESTIMONY...

NOW, NOW... NO NEED TO PANIC! WE ALREADY HAVE A GOOD IDEA WHO IT WAS!

I-IT'S NOT ME!

YOU MUST BE JOKING!

IT ALSO MEANS THAT THE PERPETRATOR IS SOMEONE WHO HAD AN APPOINTMENT TO MEET THE VICTIM TODAY-- ONE OF YOU!

THAT WOULD MEAN THE MURDER TOOK PLACE BETWEEN 3 P.M. AND 5 P.M.

IN ADDITION, CONSIDER THE FACT THAT THE VICTIM HAD A THIRD DEGREE IN IAI.

...I BELIEVE THE VICTIM FOUGHT AGAINST THE MURDERER BEFORE HE WAS KILLED.

JUDGING FROM THE RANSACKED STATE OF THE ROOM AND THE NUMEROUS SWORD WOUNDS LEFT ON THE BODY...

N-NO. YOU'VE MADE A MISTAKE!!

HEH HEH HEH. THEY SAY CRIMINALS OFTEN COME BACK TO THE SCENE OF THE CRIME. GUESS THAT WAS TRUE OF YOU TOO!

WHAT!?

THE MURDERER WOULD HAVE TO BE QUITE A SKILLED SWORDSMAN, WOULDN'T HE... MR. YUJI SUWA?

HEY, THAT'S WEIRD.

I-I COULD NEVER MURDER...

!?

LOOK. ISN'T HE HOLDING THE SWORD THE WRONG WAY?

HUH?

D-DAD!

HMPH! MEDDLING LITTLE GIRL.

TH-THAT'S TRUE.

THEY ALL HOLD THEIR BAMBOO SWORDS WITH THEIR RIGHT HANDS FORWARD AND LEFT HANDS BACK!

AT KARATE PRACTICE, I ALWAYS SEE THE KENDO TEAM PRACTICING NEXT TO US.

THAT'S NOT TRUE!

THEN THIS VICTIM MUST'VE BEEN A SOUTHPAW!

BUT THAT WOULD MEAN...

OH...

RACHEL'S RIGHT. HE'S HOLDING THE SWORD THE WRONG WAY.

HIS RIGHT HAND IS IN FRONT AND HIS LEFT IN BACK!

LOOK AT THAT PICTURE!

THE KID AGAIN!

46

EVEN IF THEY DID SWING THEIR SWORDS AT EACH OTHER, IT'S UNLIKELY THAT THERE'D BE SO MANY MARKS LEFT ON THE CEILINGS AND WALLS.

AND LOOK AT THIS ROOM.

SOMEBODY DELIBERATELY PLACED THE SWORD IN THE VICTIM'S HANDS!?

!?

WHAT !?

HE WAS TRYING TO FRAME MR. SUWA, THE IAI INSTRUCTOR!!

I SEE! THE PERPETRATOR PURPOSELY PUT SWORD MARKS ALL OVER THE ROOM TO MAKE IT APPEAR AS IF THE VICTIM HAD A SWORDFIGHT WITH SOMEBODY.

...BUT HE ALSO KNEW THAT MR. SUWA WOULD ALSO BE COMING.

IN OTHER WORDS, NOT ONLY DID THE PERPETRATOR HAVE AN APPOINTMENT WITH THE VICTIM TODAY...

BUT HE MADE A MISTAKE WHEN HE PLANTED THE SWORD IN THE VICTIM'S HANDS.

OH, NO.

TH-THAT'S TRUE.

FOR MR. MARUI'S SAKE, PLEASE ALLOW ME TO SPEAK, TOO. IT MAY HELP THE INVESTIGATION.

WAIT A SECOND, INSPECTOR!

SETTLE DOWN! EXCEPTING MR. SUWA, I WANT EACH OF YOU GENTLEMEN TO STATE YOUR NAME AND THE PURPOSE OF YOUR VISIT HERE TODAY.

M-ME NEITHER.

HEY, HEY! I DON'T EVEN KNOW THE GUY!!

I BELIEVE... THAT WAS AROUND THE TIME I WAS MEDITATING ALONE AT THE DOJO.

JUST TO BE THOROUGH, WHERE WERE YOU AT THE TIME OF THE CRIME, BETWEEN 3 P.M. AND 5 P.M.?

AS I MENTIONED EARLIER, I CAME TODAY TO GIVE MR. DENJIRO THE ¥5 MILLION I OWED HIM.

MY NAME IS YUJI SUWA. I RUN A SMALL DOJO IN THE TOWN OF BEIKA.

I HAVE THE MONEY WITH ME, AS YOU CAN SEE.

MM? ME?

WELL, OKAY THEN. NEXT!

NO, UNFORTUNATELY.

SO NOBODY CAN CORROBORATE THAT?

YUJI SUWA (AGE 46) MASTER OF SUWA DOJO

I'M IN THE SAME POSITION AS THAT GUY. I BORROWED MONEY, TOO. IN MY CASE, IT WAS ¥10 MILLION!

I'M MAKOTO AKUTSU, A SCULPTOR!!

MAKOTO AKUTSU (AGE 48) SCULPTOR

WHAT!?

...

THEN YOU DON'T HAVE AN ALIBI EITHER.

BETWEEN 3 P.M. AND 5 P.M., I WAS ALONE IN MY STUDIO WORKING ON A NEW PIECE.

N-NO. I HAD INTENDED TO, BUT I COULDN'T RAISE THE MONEY IN TIME.

SO YOU ALSO CAME HERE TO PAY HIM BACK?

I CAME TO ASK HIM FOR AN EXTENSION.

WHY NOT!? YOU'RE ONE OF THE FOUR PEOPLE WHO HAD AN APPOINTMENT WITH THE VICTIM TODAY!

INSPECTOR! D-DON'T TELL ME YOU THINK *I'M* A SUSPECT!

AND YOU, RICHARD? WHAT IN THE WORLD WERE YOU DOING HERE?

HUH?

SEE HIS WIFE INEKO OVER THERE? I WAS INVESTIGATING THE AFFAIR SHE WAS HAVING!

G-GIVE ME A BREAK! THE VICTIM HAD ASKED ME TO INVESTIGATE A CASE. I ONLY CAME TO GIVE HIM A REPORT.

WHAT?

ER, YES.

FORGET ABOUT YOU. NEXT!!

HOPELESS. A DETECTIVE WHO BLABS ABOUT THE CONTENT OF AN INVESTIGATION IN FRONT OF PEOPLE!

OOPS.

...

M- MA'AM! AN AFFAIR ...?

W-WELL...

AND? WHERE WERE YOU DURING THE TIME OF THE CRIME?

MM?

MR. MARU WAS DIABETIC AND TODAY WAS HIS CHECK-UP DAY.

MY NAME IS IKUYA HATANO. I WAS MR. MARU'S PHYSICIAN.

IKUYA HATANO (AGE 37) DOCTOR AT BEIKA HOSPITAL

...I SMELLED IT SOMEWHERE EARLIER.

WAIT A SECOND... THIS SCENT...

THIS MAN SMELLS OF SOMETHING.

IT'S A WOMAN'S PERFUME.

SNIFF

SNIFF

SNIFF

!?

OH, S-SORRY.

HOW RUDE!

HA HA HA...

OH...

WHY ARE YOU SNIFFING PEOPLE!?

COULD THAT MEAN ...

THIS IS IT! IT'S HER SCENT!!

... THESE TWO ...?

Y-YES. I WAS WATCHING A M-MOVIE IN THE GINZA DISTRICT BETWEEN 3 P.M. AND 5 P.M.

WHAT? YOU WERE WATCHING A MOVIE!?

...

G-GEE, WHAT WAS IT?

HEY, WHAT MOVIE DID YOU SEE?

HUH?

I-I DO IT A LOT... TO RELAX.

A DOCTOR WATCHING A MOVIE DURING WORK HOURS...?

WE WATCHED THAT MOVIE IN GINZA THE OTHER DAY, RIGHT?

UH, YEAH.

Y-YEAH, YEAH...

HEY, WAS IT MAYBE "SUMMER SANTA CLAUS"?

HUH?

I BET THAT'S WHAT IT WAS IF YOU SAW IT IN GINZA!

THAT'S WHAT I WATCHED TODAY! I SAW "SUMMER SANTA CLAUS."

HMM...

OH, THAT'S RIGHT! WE SAW IT ON THE LAST DAY IT WAS PLAYING.

HUH?

BUT DIDN'T THAT MOVIE END LAST WEEK?

......

NOW, TELL US THE TRUTH. WHERE WERE YOU DURING THE TIME OF THE CRIME?

ER... YOU SEE...

HOW DO YOU EXPLAIN THAT, MR. HATANO?

ER... UH...

DON'T PLAY GAMES WITH THE POLICE.

PLEASE WAIT, INSPECTOR!!

WHAT!?

YOU SEEM TONGUE-TIED. WELL, YOU'LL HAVE PLENTY OF TIME TO EXPLAIN THINGS DOWN AT THE STATION!

I KNOW, BECAUSE FROM NOON UNTIL EVENING...

D-DOCTOR HATANO IS INNOCENT!

M-MA'AM?

HOW COME...?

...

AT A H-HOTEL...?

...WE WERE TOGETHER AT THE BEIKA HOTEL!!

THIS IS THE MAN...

YOU STILL DON'T UNDERSTAND?

TUG

THIS IS THE MAN I'M HAVING AN AFFAIR WITH!

WHAT!?

FWP FWP

SEE?

LET ME SHOW YOU.

CLAK

YES, THAT'S RIGHT!

YOU MEAN TO SAY... HE'S THE MAN WHO WAS WITH YOU IN THE PHOTOS I TOOK DURING MY INVESTIGATION OF YOUR AFFAIR?

SHOVE

THIS IS THE MAN!!

...

WHAT!?

IT COULD BE THAT YOU WANTED TO INHERIT HIS FORTUNE, SO YOU KILLED HIM TOGETHER AND FRAMED MR. SUWA FOR IT!

*HMPH!* WE'LL SEE ABOUT THAT. MAYBE YOU'RE COVERING FOR EACH OTHER.

NOW YOU UNDERSTAND, DON'T YOU? HE DIDN'T KILL MY HUSBAND!!

IF I EXCLUDE RACHEL'S DAD AND THE FRAMED MR. SUWA ...

IN ANY CASE, THIS MEANS NOT ONE OF THE SUSPECTS SCHEDULED TO MEET THE VICTIM TODAY HAS AN ALIBI.

AT FOUR!

F-FIVE O'CLOCK.

*UMM,* 6 P.M., IN MY CASE.

AT 2 P.M., INSPEC-TOR!!

SO, WHAT TIME WERE YOU GUYS SCHEDULED TO MEET THE VICTIM?

... THAT LEAVES THE OTHER TWO!!

DID ONE OF THEM COMMIT THE MURDER ...?

OH, YOU DID?

I LEFT A MESSAGE ON HIS ANSWERING MACHINE SAYING I'D COME A LITTLE EARLY.

WELL, ACTUALLY ...

THAT'S STRANGE. IF I REMEMBER CORRECTLY, WE ARRIVED HERE JUST AFTER FIVE O'CLOCK AND THEN ALL OF YOU GENTLEMEN ARRIVED TOGETHER.

MY HUSBAND ALWAYS MADE HIS IMPORTANT CALLS FROM HERE.

I-I THINK IT'S HERE IN THE ANNEX.

MA'AM. WHERE IS THIS ANSWERING MACHINE?

A-ACTUALLY, I DID TOO!! I SAID I'D BE A LITTLE LATE!!

I-I LEFT A MESSAGE ON THE MACHINE TOO!!

I BELIEVE IT WAS ON THE DESK.

HERE IT IS !!

I F-FOUND IT!!

OUR APPOINTMENT IS AT FIVE SO I GUESS I'LL HEAD OVER ANYWAY. WELL THEN.

CLICK

4:38 P.M. ...

OH, THAT'S ME!!

I CAN TELL.

BEEEP

ER, IT'S HATANO. ARE YOU THERE, MR. MARU? DARN, WHAT'LL I DO...

WELL LET'S TAKE A LISTEN.

WHEEEEN

MR. AKUTSU, YOURS IS NOT IN HERE.

HUH?

...WELL THEN, SEE YOU LATER...

CLICK

4:41 P.M....

BEEEP

SUWA HERE. I WAS SCHEDULED TO SEE YOU AT SIX, BUT I THINK I'LL COME BY A LITTLE EARLY.

BY THE WAY, ABOUT NEXT MONTH'S DEGREE TEST...

DID YOU REALLY LEAVE ONE?

N-NO, THAT CAN'T BE...!

CLACK...

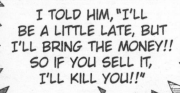

I TOLD HIM, "I'LL BE A LITTLE LATE, BUT I'LL BRING THE MONEY!! SO IF YOU SELL IT, I'LL KILL YOU!!"

I'M NOT LYING!! I REALLY DID CALL!!

MM?

THE LAST TIME I WAS HERE, IT WAS IN THIS ANNEX.

IT'S MY TEACHER'S MASTERPIECE.

WHAT KIND OF SCULPTURE IS IT?

W-WELL... HE HAD THREATENED ME. HE SAID IF I COULDN'T PAY, HE'D SELL THE SCULPTURE HE SEIZED FROM ME AS COLLATERAL.

KILL...?

IT'S THAT DRAGON!!

YES! IT'S SAFE!!

THERE IT IS!!

OH!

!?

THERE'S SOMETHING WRONG WITH THIS SCULPTURE!

HMM.

# FILE 4: THE MYSTERY OF THE ANSWERING MACHINE

YES! IT'S SAFE!!

MR. MARU SEIZED THAT DRAGON FROM YOU AS COLLATERAL FOR YOUR DEBT?

YEAH. FOR ME IT'S A TREASURE MORE PRECIOUS THAN LIFE ITSELF.

HUH!?

WOW! YOU WERE SURE LUCKY, MISTER!

...

THANK GOODNESS, THERE'S NOT ONE SCRATCH ON IT!

DON'T YOU THINK SO? EVERYTHING IN THIS ROOM GOT SCRATCHED UP BY THE SWORDS!

IT'S LIKE A MIRACLE THAT ONLY THE DRAGON WAS LEFT UNHARMED!

!?

Y-YEAH...

BOY, YOU WERE SURE LUCKY!

LOOK! THE OTHER OBJECTS NEAR THE DRAGON ARE ALL BASHED TO PIECES!

MR. AKUTSU, EVERYTHING MAKES SENSE NOW.

HEH HEH HEH. I SEE IT NOW.

WHAT!?

YOU ARE THE MURDERER!!!

THAT UNSCRATCHED DRAGON IS PROOF!!!

!?

ONE MISTAKE WAS THAT YOU PUT THE VICTIM'S HANDS IN THE WRONG POSITION WHEN YOU ARRANGED HIS HANDS ON THE SWORD HANDLE.

YOUR OTHER MISTAKE...

AH, BUT YOU MADE TWO MISTAKES IN DOING SO!!

YOU WANTED IT TO LOOK LIKE THE MURDERER AND THE VICTIM HAD ENGAGED IN A SWORD FIGHT!!

YOU THRASHED THE ROOM AND PLANTED THE SWORD IN THE VICTIM'S HANDS.

YOU TRIED TO FRAME MR. SUWA TO DEFLECT SUSPICIONS FROM YOURSELF, KNOWING HE'S A SKILLED SWORDS-MAN.

N-NO! THAT'S JUST A COINCIDENCE!!

HMPH! FOR YOU IT'S A TREASURE MORE PRECIOUS THAN LIFE!! SURE, YOU COULD KILL A MAN...BUT YOU COULDN'T BRING YOURSELF TO HARM THE SCULPTURE!!

...WAS THAT YOU LEFT YOUR DRAGON SCULPTURE UNSCRATCHED!!!

BUT I DIDN'T LIE! I REALLY DID LEAVE A MESSAGE!!

THEN WHY DID YOU LIE ABOUT LEAVING A MESSAGE ON THE ANSWERING MACHINE?

THREE MESSAGES!?

THERE WAS NO THIRD MESSAGE!

THE OTHER WAS MR. SUWA'S AT 4:41.

ONE WAS MR. HATANO'S AT 4:38.

THERE WERE ONLY TWO MESSAGES.

THE SECOND AND THIRD CALLS CAME SHORTLY AFTER 4:30.

I THINK... THE FIRST CALL WAS AROUND 3:30.

THAT'S RIGHT! THE VICTIM AND THE SUSPECT CAME INTO THIS ANNEX AROUND 3 P.M. THE VICTIM WAS FOUND DEAD AT 5 P.M. DURING THOSE TWO HOURS, THERE WERE THREE PHONE CALLS!!

WHY DID HE LET THE ANSWERING MACHINE GET IT?

AND ANYWAY, THE VICTIM WAS INSIDE THE ANNEX THEN.

THEN WAS THE FIRST CALL REALLY FROM MR. AKUTSU?

JUDGING FROM THE TIME, THE SECOND AND THIRD CALLS MUST'VE BEEN FROM MR. HATANO AND MR. SUWA.

BUT THAT FIRST CALL ...

WAIT A SECOND. I REMEMBER THE SECOND AND THIRD CALLS STOPPED RINGING QUICKLY.

!?

WHEN I FINALLY THOUGHT I'D GOTTEN THROUGH, IT WAS THE ANSWERING MACHINE.

Y-YEAH... COME TO THINK OF IT, IT RANG FOREVER.

HEY, MISTER! WAS THERE ANYTHING STRANGE WHEN YOU CALLED?

NOW THAT YOU MENTION IT, YEAH.

REMEMBER, DAD? NOBODY WAS GETTING THE PHONE AND WE WEREN'T SURE WHAT TO DO.

COULD THAT HAVE BEEN THAT FIRST CALL THAT KEPT RINGING AND RINGING?

YOU KNOW, LIKE MAYBE YOU COULDN'T GET THROUGH OR SOMETHING?

HMPH! WAIT, AND I'LL CHECK IT AGAIN!!

WHEEEN

I TOLD YOU! IT'S EXACTLY HOW I SAID!

W-WELL, WHEN IT'S NOT PICKED UP AFTER 10 OR MORE RINGS, IT AUTOMATICALLY SWITCHES OVER TO THE ANSWERING MACHINE.

MA'AM! HOW DOES THIS ANSWERING MACHINE WORK?

BY THE WAY, ABOUT NEXT MONTH'S DEGREE TEST...

BEEEP

SUWA HERE. I WAS SCHEDULED TO SEE YOU AT SIX, BUT I THINK I'LL COME BY A LITTLE EARLY.

OUR APPOINTMENT IS AT FIVE SO I GUESS I'LL HEAD OVER ANYWAY. WELL THEN.

CLICK

4:38 P.M....

BEEEP

ER, IT'S HATANO. ARE YOU THERE, MR. MARU? DARN, WHAT'LL I DO...

IT WAS J-JUST A LITTLE BIT BEFORE MY APPOINTMENT. I THINK IT MUST'VE BEEN BEFORE FOUR.

WHAT TIME DID YOU CALL EXACTLY?

THERE IS NO MESSAGE FROM YOU BEFORE OR AFTER THESE.

TH-THAT CAN'T BE.

...WELL THEN, SEE YOU LATER... CLICK 4:41 P.M. ...

CLACK

"SO IF YOU SELL THAT SCULPTURE OF THE DRAGON..."

I REALLY DID LEAVE A MESSAGE!! I SAID, "I'LL BE A LITTLE LATE, BUT I'LL BRING THE MONEY!!"

THAT'S HOW YOU CAME UP WITH THAT LIE!

N-NO...

HAHAA. I BET YOU WERE AT THE SCENE OF THIS MURDEROUS CRIME WHEN YOU HEARD THE PHONE RINGING FOR SUCH A LONG TIME!

...

"...I'LL ...I'LL KILL YOU."

BESIDES... THERE'S SOMETHING FUNNY ABOUT THE THREE MEN'S APPOINTMENT TIMES.

BUT THERE IS NO MESSAGE FROM HIM IN THE ANSWERING MACHINE.

SOMETHING'S STRANGE. IF HE REALLY IS THE MURDERER, WHY WOULD HE TELL A LIE THAT COULD ACTUALLY IMPLICATE HIM?

BUT THERE'S NO MESSAGE FROM HIM.

MR. AKUTSU'S WAS AT FOUR. HE CLAIMS TO HAVE SAID, "I'LL BE A LITTLE LATE."

MR. SUWA'S WAS AT SIX. HE SAID, "I'LL COME BY A LITTLE EARLY."

MR. HATANO'S APPOINTMENT WAS AT FIVE. HIS MESSAGE SAID, "I GUESS I'LL HEAD OVER."

ONE OF THEM MUST HAVE COME HERE AT THREE!

EXCLUDING RACHEL'S DAD, THESE THREE PEOPLE WERE THE ONLY ONES SCHEDULED TO MEET THE VICTIM TODAY.

BUT I'M SURE I SAW A POSSIBLE MURDERER COMING TO VISIT THE VICTIM AT THREE!

AND ALL THREE ARRIVED A LITTLE PAST FIVE, JUST AFTER THE BODY WAS FOUND.

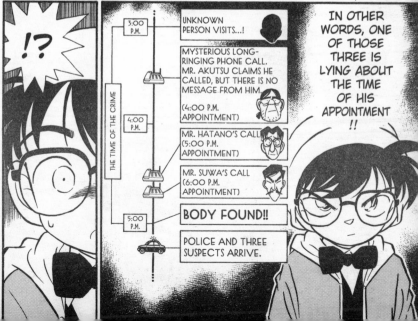

!?

THE TIME OF THE CRIME

3:00 P.M. — UNKNOWN PERSON VISITS...!

MYSTERIOUS LONG-RINGING PHONE CALL. MR. AKUTSU CLAIMS HE CALLED, BUT THERE IS NO MESSAGE FROM HIM.

(4:00 P.M. APPOINTMENT)

4:00 P.M. — MR. HATANO'S CALL (5:00 P.M. APPOINTMENT)

MR. SUWA'S CALL (6:00 P.M. APPOINTMENT)

5:00 P.M. — BODY FOUND!!

POLICE AND THREE SUSPECTS ARRIVE.

IN OTHER WORDS, ONE OF THOSE THREE IS LYING ABOUT THE TIME OF HIS APPOINTMENT!!

THINK ABOUT IT! INSPECTOR, IF I WAS THE MURDERER I WOULD'VE TAKEN THAT DRAGON SCULPTURE BACK HOME WITH ME!!

HMPH... YOU COULD HAVE TAKEN SOMETHING ELSE.

THEN THE MURDERER...

WAIT A SECOND... ONE OF THE THREE LEFT A STRANGE MESSAGE.

A NORMAL PERSON WOULDN'T SAY IT LIKE THAT.

!?

TUG

I THINK THE KEY TO THE SAFE IS INSIDE THE TANSU CHEST.

MA'AM, WERE THERE ANY VALUABLES IN THIS ROOM?

WHAT!?

IT'S G-GONE! THE KEY TO THE SAFE IS GONE!!

BUT THAT'S STRANGE... MY HUSBAND ALWAYS KEPT IT IN THIS ONE.

.....

MA'AM...!

OH, H-HERE IT IS. IT WAS IN A DIFFERENT DRAWER.

I DIDN'T!

YOU'D BETTER NOT HAVE...

...
THAT
MEANS
...

THEY
DON'T
CONNECT
!!

THE
SCRATCH
MARKS!

HEY!

TCH.

NOW SHOO. ISN'T IT BEDTIME, BOY?

HEY! DON'T TOUCH ANY-THING KID.

... MAYBE ...!?

CLANK

BABUMP
BABUMP

MM?

OH, RIGHT! I'LL GET IT RIGHT AWAY!

THE INSPECTOR OVER THERE WANTS TO BORROW IT!

Y-YES, BUT ...

EXCUSE-ME! DO YOU HAVE A POLAROID CAMERA IN THE HOUSE?

WHAT'S IT FOR?

GRIN

PHEW. NOW WITH THIS CUTTER...

KLIK KLIK

RUSTLE

TA TA TA

HURRY!

I'LL JUST GO DELIVER THIS TO THE INSPECTOR.

...

HERE IT IS, YOUNG MAN! WILL THIS DO?

YEAH, IT'S PERFECT!

ALL RIGHT. NOW'S MY CHANCE TO TAKE A QUICK PHOTO OF THIS CHEST.

FLASH

SAY CHEE--

H-HEY, HEY...

MR. POLICEMAN! LET ME TAKE ONE OF YOU!

SMILE! SMILE!

SHFF

NOT YOU AGAIN, KID!?

WHAT THE--!?

ZHOOP

QUIT GOOFING OFF! YOU'RE ON DUTY!!

ROTTEN KID.

OW.

I-INSPECTOR...

BONK

DARN

NOW SCAT!

YOU'RE IN THE WAY!

SHOO

WHERE'D YOU GET THIS CAMERA!?

YES! IT WORKED!

OH WELL... I GOT THE PHOTO I NEEDED.

THP THP THP

THP

KLIK KLIK

NOW WITH THIS CUTTER...

71

THE SWORD MARKS ALL OVER THE ROOM WEREN'T MADE JUST TO FRAME MR. SUWA.

I KNEW IT! THAT'S WHAT IT WAS!!

THEY SERVED *ANOTHER PURPOSE!*

!!

AS USUAL, I'LL HAVE THE OLD MAN ...

ALL RIGHT. I'LL USE THIS WRISTWATCH STUN GUN.

SIDLE

I'D BETTER TELL THE INSPECTOR ABOUT THIS RIGHT AWAY.

POINK

FWSH

... TAKE A NAP.

BLIP ...

NOW I'LL SET MY BOW-TIE VOICE MODULATOR TO HIS VOICE.

ZZZ...

D-DAD?

THWUMP

SKOOCH

WBBL

SCHLUMP

DASH

CLICK CLICK

FOR NOW... FINE, FINE.

I'D LIKE TO GO, TOO.

ER... MAY I GO NOW? I STILL HAVE WORK TO DO.

TCH!

W-W-WAIT ...

NOW, MR. AKUTSU! WHY DON'T YOU COME WITH ME TO THE STATION!?

BUT I'M SURE YOU'LL END UP RELEASING ME FOR LACK OF EVIDENCE!!

FINE! TAKE ME TO THE STATION!!

RICHARD ...?

HUH?

HOLD IT RIGHT THERE !!!

A C-CLEVER ...?

THIS TIME I KNOW FOR CERTAIN, INSPECTOR.

I'VE DISCOVERED THE IDENTITY OF THE MURDER. HE PLAYED A CLEVER TRICK, INDEED.

... MR. MARU.

I KNOW WHO MURDERED ...

SHFF

YES. HE USED THAT TRICK TO FOOL US.

OH... YOU MEAN HOW HE RANSACKED THE ROOM TO MAKE IT LOOK LIKE THERE WAS A SWORD FIGHT?

IT WAS YOU !!!

BAM

THE CIRCUMSTANCES OF THE CRIME IMPLICATED MR. AKUTSU AS THE PRIME SUSPECT.

THE SUSPECTS ARE THE THREE MEN WHO HAD APPOINTMENTS WITH MR. MARU THAT DAY-- IKUYA HATANO, YUJI SUWA AND MAKOTO AKUTSU.

MR. DENJIRO MARU WAS BRUTALLY MURDERED IN THE ANNEX BUILDING OF HIS RESIDENCE.

NOW HE WAS ABOUT TO UNRAVEL THE MYSTERY USING RICHARD MOORE'S VOICE.

BUT CONAN SAW THROUGH THE TRICK AND DISCOVERED THE REAL IDENTITY OF THE MURDERER.

# FILE 5: THE TESTIMONY OF THE TANSU CHEST

THAT'S RIGHT.

Y-YOU KNOW WHO DID IT?

BAM

BUT I KNOW WHO MURDERED MR. DENJIRO MARU!

HE USED A CLEVER TRICK TO FOOL US.

SHFF

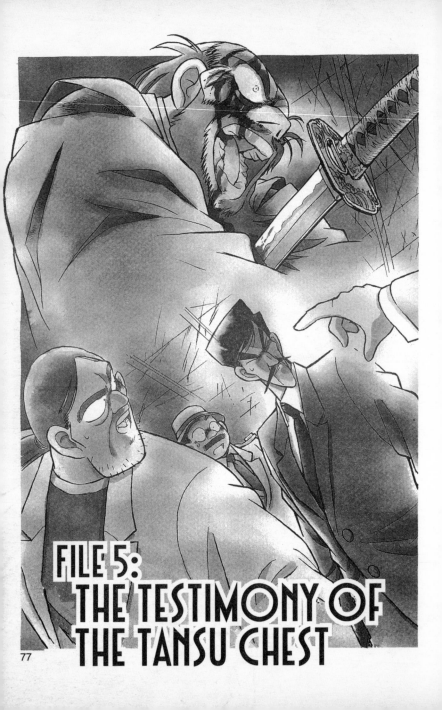

# FILE 5:
# THE TESTIMONY OF
# THE TANSU CHEST

COME ON, RICHARD. WHAT ARE YOU SAYING?

M-MR. SUWA...?

.....

BESIDES, THE VICTIM WAS HOLDING THE SWORD THE WRONG WAY!!

YEAH, DAD!! EVEN IF A SWORD FIGHT REALLY HAPPENED, THERE WOULDN'T BE SO MANY SLASH MARKS LEFT ALL OVER THE ROOM.

HE WANTED IT TO LOOK LIKE HE WAS KILLED AFTER A SWORD FIGHT!!

THE PERPETRATOR PUT A SWORD IN THE VICTIM'S HANDS AND SCRATCHED UP THE ROOM TO IMPLICATE MR. SUWA.

AHA...

MR. SUWA IS A SWORDSMAN. HE WOULDN'T MAKE A MISTAKE LIKE THAT.

THAT WAS MR. SUWA'S PLAN.

THAT'S HOW WE WERE FOOLED.

MR. SUWA, A SKILLED SWORDS-MAN, DID THAT PRECISELY TO SHIFT SUSPICION ONTO HIMSELF.

YES... HE RANSACKED THE ROOM AND PLANTED THE SWORD IN THE VICTIM'S HANDS, MAKING IT APPEAR AS IF THERE WAS A FIGHT.

THAT WAS HIS WAY OUT!!

HE MADE AN EXCESSIVE NUMBER OF SWORD MARKS ALL OVER THE ROOM AND INTENTIONALLY REVERSED THE VICTIM'S GRIP ON THE SWORD.

YES, BUT HE HAD TAKEN PRECAUTIONS.

ONTO HIMSELF ...?

HE KNEW THAT WOULD IMMEDIATELY CLEAR HIS NAME FROM THE LIST OF SUSPECTS!!

MR. SUWA DELIBERATELY MADE IT APPEAR AS IF SOMEBODY HAD TRIED TO FRAME HIM.

YOU RAISE AN INTERESTING POINT, DETECTIVE MOORE.

HMPH.

...

AFTER ALL, WHO WOULD SUSPECT HIM OF DEVISING A PLAN THAT WOULD CAST SUSPICION ON HIMSELF!?

THE DRAGON WAS LEFT UNTOUCHED IN THE MIDST OF THIS RANSACKED ROOM.

AND HOW DO YOU EXPLAIN THE SCULPTURE?

TH-THAT'S RIGHT.

BUT THAT IS MERELY A THEORY. YOU HAVE NO EVIDENCE THAT PROVES I DID IT.

IT'S MORE PLAUSIBLE TO THINK MR. AKUTSU DID IT. HE RANSACKED THE ROOM BUT COULDN'T BRING HIMSELF TO DAMAGE THE SCULPTURE.

THAT'S THE PRECIOUS SCULPTURE THE VICTIM TOOK FROM MR. AKUTSU AS COLLATERAL FOR HIS DEBT.

A-ACTUALLY, INSPECTOR ...

HUH?

SHOVE

AGH!

SLIP

YOU BROUGHT UP THAT THEORY YOURSELF, RICHARD.

MR. AKUTSU SAID HIMSELF THAT WE HAVE NEVER MET BEFORE.

HA HA HA... YOU MUST BE KIDDING.

HOW COULD I HAVE KNOWN THAT WAS HIS SCULPTURE?

HE LEFT THE DRAGON UNTOUCHED TO CAST SUSPICION ON MR. AKUTSU.

I SUSPECT IT WAS MR. SUWA'S DOING.

WHAT!?

A SET-UP?

THAT WAS A SET-UP.

NOD...

80

YOU KNOW... MR. AKUTSU LEFT THAT MESSAGE SAYING, "IF YOU SELL THAT SCULPTURE, I'LL KILL YOU."

WHAT...?

THE ANSWERING MACHINE.

THAT GAVE HIM THE IDEA OF PUTTING THE BLAME ON MR. AKUTSU.

I'LL KILL YOU!!

MR. SUWA PROBABLY HEARD THAT WHILE HE WAS STILL AT THE SCENE OF THE MURDER.

MR. AKUTSU'S MESSAGE WAS RECORDED AT THE TIME OF CRIME. IF LEFT BEHIND, IT COULD ESTABLISH AN ALIBI FOR MR. AKUTSU.

MR. SUWA REWOUND THE TAPE AND ERASED IT. HE RECORDED HIS OWN MESSAGE ON TOP OF IT.

MR. AKUTSU CLAIMS TO HAVE LEFT THAT MESSAGE, BUT IN ACTUAL FACT, THERE WAS NO SUCH MESSAGE RECORDED.

FURTHERMORE...

NO. THERE IS A CRUCIAL DIFFERENCE BETWEEN HIS MESSAGE AND YOURS.

COULDN'T HE HAVE DONE THE SAME TOO?

BUT THAT DOCTOR HATANO LEFT ONE BEFORE I DID.

I DID INDEED LEAVE A MESSAGE ON THE ANSWERING MACHINE.

WAIT A SECOND.

IN YOUR MESSAGE YOU GIVE YOURSELF AWAY AS THE MURDERER !!!

!?

DO YOU SEE?

SUWA HERE. I WAS SCHEDULED TO SEE YOU AT SIX, BUT I THINK I'LL COME BY A LITTLE EARLY.

IN CONTRAST, LISTEN TO MR. SUWA'S MESSAGE.

OUR APPOINTMENT IS AT FIVE SO I GUESS I'LL HEAD OVER ANYWAY. WELL THEN.

BEEEP

ER, IT'S HATANO. ARE YOU THERE, MR. MARU? DARN, WHAT'LL I DO...

MR. HATANO SAID ...

WHO WOULD GO EARLY TO MEET SOMEBODY AT THEIR HOME WHEN THEY KNOW THEY'RE NOT THERE?

I CAN UNDERSTAND MR. HATANO SAYING, "I GUESS I'LL HEAD OVER ANYWAY."

UH, SEE WHAT?

BUT MR. SUWA SAID HE WOULD GO EARLIER THAN SCHEDULED.

82

THAT IS, HE KNEW HIS DEAD BODY WAS HERE IN THE ANNEX!!

MR. SUWA KNEW MR. MARU WAS HOME.

...

OH, THAT'S RIGHT...!

TO THINK THAT'S THE TRUMP CARD OF THE GREAT DETECTIVE SO LAUDED IN THE NEWSPAPERS.

I'M DISAPPOINTED IN YOU, DETECTIVE MOORE.

...

I FIGURED HE WOULD BE HOME AT FIVE.

THAT'S WHY I THOUGHT IT WOULD BE ALL RIGHT IF I ENDED UP COMING EARLIER THAN MY APPOINTMENT AT SIX.

HE SAID HE WAS MEETING PEOPLE AT HIS HOME AT FOUR AND AT FIVE SO HE WANTED TO SCHEDULE OUR MEETING OUTSIDE OF THOSE TIMES.

WHEN MR. MARU AND I WERE DECIDING ON A TIME TO MEET, THIS IS WHAT HE TOLD ME.

HEH HEH HEH. I HAVE NO DOUBTS.

SURELY YOU NO LONGER DOUBT ME!

NOW, DETECTIVE MOORE.

I WANTED TO RETURN THE MONEY I OWED HIM AS SOON AS I COULD.

AND WHY DID YOU COME EARLY?

YOU **ARE** THE MURDERER !!!

I AM ENTIRELY CONFIDENT !!

WHAT !?

NO. IT WAS TO HIDE SOMETHING.

THE REASON THE KILLER THRASHED THE ROOM WITH A SWORD WAS NOT TO MAKE IT LOOK LIKE THERE'D BEEN A FIGHT.

IT'S RIGHT HERE IN THIS ROOM-- INDISPUTABLE EVIDENCE THAT YOU MURDERED MR. MARU.

H-HERE? WHERE?

IT'S RIGHT NEXT TO YOU, INSPECTOR.

HIDE SOMETHING?

THE SCRATCHES ON THE CHEST!!

!?

WHY DON'T YOU PUT THEM BACK IN PLACE?

THE MURDERER INTENTIONALLY REARRANGED THE DRAWERS.

SEE? THE SCRATCHES DON'T CONNECT.

TAKE A GOOD LONG LOOK.

T-TRUE...

WHAT!?

NOW SWAP THE SECOND DRAWER FROM THE LEFT IN THE 3RD ROW WITH THE FAR RIGHT DRAWER IN THE 4TH ROW.

LASTLY, SWITCH THE 2ND DRAWER FROM THE LEFT IN THE 5TH ROW WITH THE 3RD DRAWER FROM THE LEFT IN THE 4TH ROW.

IN THE 2ND ROW, TAKE THE 2ND DRAWER FROM THE LEFT AND EXCHANGE IT WITH THE FAR RIGHT DRAWER IN THAT ROW.

NEXT, EXCHANGE THE FAR LEFT DRAWER IN THE 2ND ROW WITH THE FAR LEFT DRAWER IN THE 5TH ROW.

IN THE TOP ROW, SWAP THE SECOND DRAWER FROM THE LEFT WITH THE FAR RIGHT DRAWER.

THAT SAYS SUWA!!

STILL, THE SCRATCHED UP CHEST OF DRAWERS WOULD ATTRACT TOO MUCH ATTENTION.

WHEN MR. SUWA SAW IT, HE REARRANGED THE DRAWERS AND PUT MORE SCRATCHES OVER IT TO MAKE THE LETTERS INDISTING-UISHABLE.

I BET HE USED HIS SWORD TO DO IT WHILE MR. SUWA'S ATTENTION WAS DRAWN AWAY BY MR. AKUTSU'S PHONE CALL.

SKRII SKRII

BRRRING!

THE VICTIM MUST HAVE SCRATCHED HIS KILLER'S NAME INTO THE WOOD AS HE WAS DYING.

IT WAS TO KEEP US FROM NOTICING MR. MARU'S DYING WORD, SCRATCHED INTO THE CHEST OF DRAWERS!!

THAT'S WHY YOU PUT SWORD MARKS ALL OVER THE ROOM!!

SO WHY ...?

HE BROUGHT THE MONEY HE OWED TO THE VICTIM.

BUT WHY ...?

.....

...IT WAS... THE SWORD.

*HMPH.* IT'S NOT SOME DULL SWORD LIKE THAT.

DON'T TELL ME IT'S THE SWORD YOU USED AS THE MURDER WEAPON!

I, TOO, HAD LEFT SOMETHING WITH MR. MARU AS COLLATERAL FOR MY DEBT. IN MY CASE, IT WAS A SWORD.

SWORD ...?

OH, THAT SWORD ?

SUCH A SWORD... AND YET...

THIS SWORD WAS PASSED DOWN FROM GENERATION TO GENERATION IN THE SUWA FAMILY.

IT WAS THE CELEBRATED SWORD, "KIKUCHIYO" !!!

I'LL KEEP THE MONEY I GOT FROM THE SALE AS INTEREST ON THE MONEY YOU OWE ME.

...

IT DIDN'T FETCH MUCH, THOUGH.

I SOLD IT OFF.

!?

YES.

BEFORE I KNEW IT, I'D GRABBED THE SWORD DISPLAYED IN THE ALCOVE AND DELIVERED A HEAVY SWING TO HIS BACK.

HUH?

... KIND OF ...

IT WAS ...

DASH

GRAB

AAGH!

... LIKE THIS !!!

A A A A A A...

TUD

YOU DIDN'T EVEN FLINCH WHEN I SWUNG THE SWORD AT YOU.

I... AM IMPRESSED.

I LET MY GUARD DOWN THINKING HE DIED FROM MY FIRST SWING, AND WHILE MY BACK WAS TURNED HE WROTE MY NAME.

SHOOP

THE REST WAS JUST AS YOU SAID.

HMPH.

GOOD-BYE.

IT SEEMS THE BIGGEST MISCALCULATION I MADE WAS THE FACT THAT YOU WERE HERE!

YOU ARE INDEED A GREAT DETECTIVE, MR. RICHARD MOORE!!

OOH.

HUH?

DRIP

HEY, THERE'S SOMETHING ON YOUR HEAD.

...

I HAVE A NEW RESPECT FOR YOU, RICHARD!!

WOW, DAD!!

BY THE WAY, THE OLD MAN'S WOUND WAS A TINY CUT ABOUT 3 MILLIMETERS DEEP.

AAAAAAARRRRGH!

CALL AN AMBULANCE!!

I'M DYING!!

IT'S BLOOD!!

?

# FILE 6: THE JUNIOR DETECTIVE LEAGUE!

TEITAN ELEMENTARY SCHOOL

HEY CONAN! REMEMBER YOUR PROMISE? ARE YOU ALMOST DONE WITH THEM?

REMEMBER? YOU SAID IT YOURSELF THAT IF I COULD BEAT YOU AT THAT GAME YOU'D MAKE ME ANYTHING!

C'MON! DID YOU FORGET WHAT YOU PROMISED AT THE ARCADE?

DONE WITH WHAT?

YEAH, YEAH! YOU WEREN'T AS GOOD AS YOU SAID YOU WERE.

IT'S CRIMINAL TO BREACH A CONTRACT!

TH-THAT'S LOW!!

WHAT !!?

THAT WAS SO LONG AGO I FORGOT.

HA HA HA ...

I LET MY GUARD DOWN SINCE THEY'RE JUST KIDS.

JUST KIDDING.

SEE? DETECTIVE BADGES!!

I HAVE THEM RIGHT HERE!

CLANK

THERE'S A TRANSMITTER IN IT TOO!!

IT'S GOT A BUILT-IN SUPER MINI TRANSCEIVER!!

WELL, I GUESS IT'S PERFECT FOR KIDS PLAYING DETECTIVES.

I ASKED DOC AGASA TO MAKE THEM.

DID YOU MAKE THIS YOURSELF, CONAN?

JUNIOR DETECTIVE LEAGUE! THAT WOULD BE US!

WHOA! COOL!!

SO...?

DON'T YOU KNOW WE'RE THE JUNIOR DETECTIVE LEAGUE?

WHAT'D YOU THINK!

HUH? START WHAT...?

ALL RIGHT GUYS! LET'S START RIGHT AWAY!

YAY!

WE HAVE JUST FORMED THE JUNIOR DETECTIVE LEAGUE!

WE INTERRUPT YOUR LUNCH FOR AN IMPORTANT ANNOUNCEMENT.

HELLO, EVERYBODY!!

WE'RE IN FIRST GRADE, CLASS B. I'M GEORGE KOJIMA, LEADER OF THE JUNIOR DETECTIVE LEAGUE.

STUMPED? PUZZLED? JUST COME TO US!

WE WILL BE ACCEPTING NEW CASES AFTER SCHOOL FROM FIVE TO SIX.

P.A. Room

AND I'M CONAN EDOGAWA.

I'M THE CUTE GIRL DETECTIVE AMY YOSHIDA.

I'M THE NIHILISTIC DETECTIVE MITCH TSUBURAYA.

WE'LL SOLVE ANYTHING!!!

RRRRRRRRRRRRING

MAYBE WE DIDN'T ADVERTISE ENOUGH?

SIGH

YEAH.

NOBODY'S COMING.

TONK TONK

G-GEORGE!!

SNAP

MAN, I QUIT. I QUIT!! THIS IS TOO BORING. I'M OUTTA HERE!!

CONAN EVEN WENT TO THE TROUBLE OF GIVING US THESE BADGES.

.....

WHAT DO YOU EXPECT! IF IT WERE THAT EASY TO GET CLIENTS, DETECTIVES WOULD BE LIVING THE EASY LIFE!

TONK

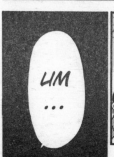

UM ...

B-BUT ...

C'MON, MITCH! LET'S GO PLAY VIDEO GAMES!!

96

THERE'S SOMETHING I WANT TO ASK YOU GUYS.

HUH?

N-NO. IT'S AKIRA. HE'S BEEN MISSING SINCE LAST NIGHT.

YOU WANT US TO INVESTIGATE YOUR PARENTS' AFFAIRS!

WHAT? A MURDER!?

FRAUD!?

I HAVE A PICTURE.

WHAT DOES HE LOOK LIKE?

PERHAPS HE WAS KIDNAPPED!

A MISSING PERSONS CASE!!!

WHAT!?

!?

BAM

HERE!

YEAH.

YOU WERE TALKING ABOUT A CAT!?

A... CAT?

.....

TO BAD IT WASN'T A KIDNAPPING.

B-BUT ...

I'M SURE THE CAT WILL COME BACK IF YOU WAIT!

SORRY! WE ONLY ACCEPT MORE COMPLEX CASES!!

O-ONLY ¥10 ...!?

I'LL PAY EACH OF YOU ¥10.

AND I WAS EVEN THINKING OF GIVING YOU GUYS KAMEN YAIBA CARDS, TOO.

MUTTER

HMPH.

RATTLE

NOW GO AWAY! GO AWAY!

SEE! I COLLECT THEM!!

WHAT?

... HYPER GOLDEN CARD!!

THIS IS THE RARE AND LEGENDARY ...

NOT ONLY THAT ...

KAMEN YAIBA CARDS!?

WOW!

I CAN'T BELIEVE YOU GUYS.

WE'LL TAKE THE CASE!!!

THAT'S STRANGE. HE ONLY DISAPPEARED YESTERDAY SO HE SHOULD STILL BE AROUND HERE.

CAW CAW

DARN. HE'S NOWHERE TO BE FOUND.

...AKIRA'S MEOW IS DIFFERENT FROM OTHER CATS.

HE GOES, "GYAAGO."

OH, WELL ACTUALLY...

HEY, DOES THE CAT HAVE ANY HABITS OR CHARAC- TERISTICS?

NO! YOU'VE GOTTA FIND HIM!!

HEY! WE'VE WORKED PLENTY HARD SO HOW 'BOUT GIVING US THE CARD ALREADY!

100

...

YEAH, YEAH. JUST LIKE THAT.

GYAAGO

HUH ?

AKIRA !?

AKIRA !?

FROM THAT HOUSE !

WH-WHERE'D THAT COME FROM?

YES !!!

OH, AKIRA !!

PEEK

GYAAGO

WHAT!?

!?

WE'D BETTER TREAT HIM QUICKLY!

...

HE'S ALL BLOODY.

HOP

HUH?

TROT TROT TROT

THAT MEANS THE BLOOD ON THE CAT IS--

NO. THIS CAT IS NOT INJURED!!

UHGG
...

KCHAK

SKREEECH

IT'S T-TRUE!!

YOU REALLY SAW A BODY?

THERE'S NO MISTAKE, INSPECTOR.

Y-YES!!

OH, IT'S YOU KIDS. YOU CALLED THE POLICE?

IN OTHER WORDS, THE BODY IS STILL INSIDE.

AND SINCE THE TIME WE DISCOVERED THE BODY, NOBODY HAS ENTERED OR EXITED THE HOUSE.

C-CONAN.

IT'S THE POLICE. OPEN UP!!

DING DONG DING DONG

YES SIR!!

ALL RIGHT, LET'S GO IN!!

CREAK

A DEAD BODY!?

THESE KIDS CLAIM THEY SAW A DEAD BODY IN YOUR HOUSE.

WHAT IS IT? WHAT'S ALL THE NOISE?

KCHAK

HE HAD COLLAPSED AND WAS ALL BLOODY!!

A M-MAN IN THE BATH-TUB!

WE SAW IT!!

!

THE BATH-ROOM IS AT THE END OF THE HALL.

I MYSELF WAS TAKING A BATH JUST NOW.

TCH. THIS IS INSANE.

RATTLE

H-HEY...

YOU WON'T MIND IF I TAKE A LOOK.

TA TA TA...

TMP

TMP

!?

THE BODY DIS-APPEARED!

I-IT'S GONE.

# FILE 7:
# MYSTERIOUS BROTHERS

THE BODY!

IT'S GONE!?

THAT'S IMPOSSIBLE!

NO!

THESE KIDS ARE JUST PLAYING A PRANK.

BUT WE REALLY SAW IT!!

THERE'S NO DEAD BODY ANYWHERE.

I TOLD YOU!

THERE WAS A BLOODY MAN COLLAPSED IN THE BATHROOM.

HE WAS DEAD!!!

HE WOULD'VE HAD TIME TO HIDE THE BODY.

HMM. WE GOT HERE ABOUT 15 MINUTES AFTER YOU KIDS CALLED.

YEAH! HE HEARD US SHOUTING WHEN WE FOUND THE BODY SO HE QUICKLY HID IT!!

WHAT!?

I BET THIS MAN HID IT!!

IT SEEMS TO ME...

HMPH.

GO AHEAD!! YOU WON'T FIND ANYTHING SUSPICIOUS HERE! IF THERE'S A PROBLEM, TELL MY YOUNGER BROTHER. HE'LL BE HOME SOON.

I'LL BE SLEEPING UPSTAIRS!!

RIDICULOUS!! LOOK AROUND AS MUCH AS YOU LIKE!!

SO YOU DON'T MIND IF WE POKE AROUND ON OUR OWN?

DID SOME-THING HAPPEN AT MY HOUSE...?

UM...

H-HELLO...

INSPECTOR! THE YOUNGER BROTHER IS HOME!!

DAMN IT. WE CAN'T FIND IT.

THEY'D BETTER NOT BE...

HEY? WHERE ARE THE OTHER THREE?

HUH? THEY WERE JUST HERE.

W-WELL, THESE KIDS HERE SAY THEY SAW A DEAD MAN IN YOUR HOME.

WHAT'S GOING ON...?

H-HEY!

DASH

HEY, CONAN!

ZSSSHH

THE JUNIOR DETECTIVE LEAGUE!!

THAT'S US!

BAM

WE'RE HELPING TO LOOK!

KIDS! YOU'RE MAKING A MESS.

I KNEW IT.

WE ARE...

KRASH

UH-OH...

HUH?

RIGHT, GEORGE!?

SLIP

114

WHAT'S ALL THAT NOISE!? KEEP IT DOWN!!

DON'T WORRY. THAT VASE ISN'T SO VALUABLE.

OOPS...

...BUT HE LOUNGES AROUND THE HOUSE MORE THAN HE WRITES.

HE'S A WRITER...

EXCUSE ME, BUT WHAT DOES YOUR OLDER BROTHER DO?

IS KAZUYOSHI UPSTAIRS?

YES. HE SEEMS QUITE UPSET.

DO YOU AND YOUR BROTHER LIVE HERE TOGETHER?

TOMOFUMI TANAKA. YOU WORK FOR A BROKERAGE FIRM?

HERE'S MY CARD.

A LEAF!?

MY BROTHER'S STAYING WITH ME.

WHAT'S THAT!?

FLIT

!?

YES, BUT THIS IS MY HOUSE.

WE LOOKED IN THE ATTIC AND UNDER THE FLOORS.

HMM...

Y-YES...

ALL THAT'S LEFT IS YOUR OLDER BROTHER'S ROOM.

I JUST HOPE HE DOESN'T MIND TOO MUCH.

PTNK

Tanaka

KNOCK KNOCK

KAZU-YOSHI?

LOOKS LIKE HE'S SLEEPING.

I-IT'S OKAY.

YOU THINK SO?

BASEBALL'S SPRING TRAINING IS FINALLY COMING TO AN END...

KAZU-YOSHI?

YES. HE DOESN'T LIKE HAVING THINGS AROUND.

WHAT A BARE ROOM.

...

WHAT KIND OF TREE IS IT?

WOW. YOU HAVE A MAGNIFICENT TREE IN THE BACK-YARD.

FWSH

I-I THINK HE HEARD ME.

HUH?

CLICK

REALLY! YOU'D THINK HE COULD AT LEAST TURN OFF THE TV IF HE'S GOING TO SLEEP.

MR. TANAKA?

WE'RE NOT LYING!!

KNOW WHAT THAT MEANS, KIDS!?

WELL, WE DIDN'T FIND ANY DEAD BODY.

I BELIEVE I'VE SHOWN YOU EVERYTHING THERE IS TO SEE.

THERE'S NO SUCH THING.

YEAH! YEAH!

THERE MUST BE A HIDDEN DOOR OR A SECRET BASEMENT!!

HUH?

MAYBE SOMEONE ALREADY TOOK THE BODY AWAY!

...

BUT I WAS ONLY WATCHING FROM THE PHONE BOOTH IN FRONT OF THE HOUSE. I COULDN'T SEE THE BACK.

YEAH, THAT'S WHAT I SAID THEN.

NOBODY WENT IN OR OUT OF THIS HOUSE.

BUT CONAN... YOU SAID IT YOURSELF WHEN WE ARRIVED.

118

IF YOU TIED THE BODY ONTO YOURSELF AND USED THAT TREE, YOU COULD GET THE BODY OVER THE FENCE.

... BUT YOU KNOW THAT TALL TREE IN THE BACK?

!?

YEAH. THAT'S WHAT I THOUGHT TOO. THAT'S WHY I SAID NOBODY WENT IN OR OUT ...

BUT THERE'S A HIGH FENCE AT THE BACK OF THE HOUSE! I CAN'T IMAGINE CLIMBING OVER THAT FENCE WITH A BODY.

HUH?

TANAKA HERE !!!

KCHAK

THE TREE! THE ONE IN THE BACK!

SO... WHAT WERE WE TALKING ABOUT?

J-JUST A WRONG NUMBER.

CLICK

DID THE PHONE RING JUST NOW?

...

OH. THAT TREE WAS THERE WHEN I BOUGHT THIS PLACE.

NO... NO... GOODBYE.

NO. THIS ISN'T THE TAKEI RESIDENCE.

IT'S NOT EASY, BUT IT CAN BE DONE.

SO IT'S POSSIBLE TO CLIMB UP WITH A BODY TIED TO YOU?

Y-YES...

HEY! YOU ALL RIGHT?

!?

THERE IS A LEDGE ABOUT 40 CENTIMETERS WIDE-- BUT IT'D BE IMPOSSIBLE FOR ANYONE LUGGING A BODY.

EVEN IF YOU DID GET DOWN, IT'S BARELY WIDE ENOUGH FOR ONE PERSON.

WHAT !?

THERE'S NO FOOT-HOLD OR ANY-THING?

WAIT A SEC, INSPECTOR !!

THERE'S AN EMBANKMENT ON THE OTHER SIDE OF THE FENCE. YOU CAN'T GET DOWN!!

WAIT, INSPECTOR!!

FORGET IT. NOTHING'S GOING TO SHOW UP.

INSPECTOR! SHOULD WE CALL FORENSICS JUST IN CASE?

IN OTHER WORDS, YOU KIDS LIED.

HMM. THERE'S NO BODY IN THE HOUSE AND WE'VE FOUND IT WOULD'VE BEEN IMPOSSIBLE TO GET IT OFF THE PROPERTY.

N-NO!

WE REALLY DID--

BANG

VROOM.

HMPH. I WAS A FOOL TO BELIEVE YOU KIDS JUST BECAUSE YOU CAUGHT THAT RING OF ITALIAN BURGLARS.

SO FAR, I CAN ONLY GUESS THAT...

HOW DID THE BODY DISAPPEAR!?

HOW!?

!?

IN THE MEANTIME, THE YOUNGER BROTHER MUST HAVE MADE PREPARATIONS TO TAKE THE BODY OUT.

...THE OLDER BROTHER PROBABLY WASHED THE DEAD BODY IN THE BATHROOM.

BUT HOW...!?

IT MIGHT BE IMPOSSIBLE FOR ONE PERSON, BUT THERE MUST HAVE BEEN A WAY FOR TWO TO DO IT.

THAT MUST MEAN HE DID USE THIS TREE TO GET THE BODY OUT.

IT'S THE SAME KIND OF LEAF AS THE ONE STUCK ON THE YOUNGER BROTHER.

HELLO.

HEY, CONAN!

HUH?

TONK

SHHH...!

OH, BROTHER.

WE CAN'T JUST STAND BY AND LET THE JUNIOR DETECTIVE LEAGUE BE ACCUSED OF LYING!!

NOT SO LOUD, GEORGE!!

G-GUYS! WHAT ARE YOU DOING!?

HE'S STILL SLEEPING IN THERE.

HUH? DID HE SEE US?

WATCH OUT. HIDE!!

SHFF

HEY...

DANG IT. HE COULD AT LEAST HAVE CLOSED THE CURTAINS.

WH-WHAT ARE WE GOING TO DO?

IT'S THAT MEAN MAN!!

W-WAIT A SECOND.

!?

MAYBE...

...I'VE BEEN MAKING A TERRIBLE MISTAKE!

# FILE 8:
# THE MYSTERY OF
# THE MOVING BODY

... A TERRIBLE MISTAKE!

... I'VE BEEN MAKING ...

MAYBE ...

F-FIGURED WHAT OUT?

I MIGHT'VE FIGURED IT OUT.

CLANK

WHAT'S WRONG?

TA TA TA...

WHOMP

THUD

C-CONAN?

WHOOSH

HUH?

THE WAY THE MURDERER HID THE BODY!!

I'M ON THE VERGE OF SOLVING THE MYSTERY OF THE DISAPPEARING BODY!!!

WE DIDN'T FIND IT INSIDE THE HOUSE WHEN WE LOOKED WITH THE POLICE, YET THEY SAID IT WOULD'VE BEEN IMPOSSIBLE TO MAKE OFF WITH IT.

YOU KNOW! THE BODY WE FOUND IN THE BATHROOM OF THIS HOUSE!

RATTLE

WOW...

SEE!

I UNLOCKED IT WHILE THE POLICE WERE BUSY LOOKING FOR THE BODY.

YEAH. FROM THE BATHROOM WINDOW!

C-CAN YOU GET IN?

SHFF

I'M GOING INSIDE TO MAKE SURE.

HE WAS STILL SLEEPING WHEN WE WERE WATCHING FROM THE TREE, BUT WHO KNOWS WHEN HE'LL WAKE UP!!

...THE PROBLEM IS THE MEAN OLDER ONE!

THE YOUNGER ONE SEEMED NICE, BUT...

BUT WILL YOU BE ALL RIGHT BY YOURSELF? THOSE TWO BROTHERS ARE STILL IN THE HOUSE!

YEAH, THAT'S THE HARD PART.

...

EVEN HIS YOUNGER BROTHER WAS REALLY SCARED.

YOU'LL BE IN BIG TROUBLE IF YOU GET CAUGHT!!

WHAT'S ALL THAT NOISE!? KEEP IT DOWN!!

THAT'S RIGHT! WHEN GEORGE BROKE THE POT HE YELLED REALLY LOUD!

YOU KNOW THE DETECTIVE BADGES I GAVE YOU GUYS?

IF I FIND THE BODY I'LL CONTACT YOU GUYS RIGHT AWAY SO YOU CAN CALL THE POLICE!!

YOU GUYS WAIT AT THE PHONE BOOTH IN FRONT OF THE HOUSE!!

CON-TACT US?

NO! THE MURDERER COULD STILL BE INSIDE!!

I GOT IT! WE'LL GO AND BACK YOU UP!!

YOU CAN RECEIVE SIGNALS BY ADJUSTING THE DIAL TO THE RIGHT FREQUENCY. TO TRANSMIT, YOU JUST PUSH THE BUTTON!!

THERE'S A MINIATURE TRANSCEIVER BUILT INTO THEM!!

CLICK FWP

H-HEY, CONAN!!

SEE YA!!

HEY...

I ADJUSTED THE FREQUENCY ON YOUR BADGES TO MATCH MINE. SO DON'T MESS WITH THE DIALS, OKAY!?

WOW...

HE LOCKED IT.

TCH...

!?

I'M IN. NOW I'VE GOT TO GET UPSTAIRS TO THAT ROOM.

THE YOUNGER BROTHER IS STILL AWAKE.

DAMN IT...

SHFF

KCHAK

DASH

TMP

WHAT IS IT !?

BAM

MM? HE TOOK SOMETHING OUT OF HIS SUIT AND PUT IT NEXT TO THE PHONE.

KCHAK

CLUNK

TROT TROT

ALL THAT'S LEFT IS TO FIND THE BODY.

HEH HEH HEH... I'M BEGINNING TO GET A READ ON THIS CASE.

I SEE... SO THAT'S HOW HE PULLED OFF THAT TRICK.

A CELL PHONE !?

THAT'S A DISTINCT POSSIBILITY. REMEMBER HOW HE TRICKED US AND WENT BACK ALL BY HIMSELF WHEN WE WERE HUNTING FOR THAT TREASURE?

HE'S NOT TRYING TO TAKE ALL THE CREDIT, IS HE?

HE SAID HE'D CALL IF HE FOUND THE BODY.

WHAT'S TAKING CONAN SO LONG?

YEAH....

NO. CONAN TOLD US TO WAIT.

THAT DOES IT! I'M GOING INSIDE!

UM... WHICH ROOM WAS IT?

SNEAK

!?

THIS IS IT. THIS IS IT.

SNEAK

KCHAK

OH!

THIS ROOM HAS BOTH AN ANSWERING MACHINE AND A VCR.

I SEE ...

I KNEW IT.

THE MYSTERY IS SOLVED !!

SLAM

PHEW ...

MUST BE MY IMAGI-NATION.

THAT'S STRANGE... I THOUGHT I HEARD SOMETHING.

FSHAA

YIKES !!

FWIP

WHAT!?

IT'S YOU WHO SHOULD GIVE UP, MR. TANAKA!!

SHOVE

IT'S...

...WAS ON THE CHAIR IN THIS ROOM, WATCHING TV.

YES... THE BODY...

...BUT IT WAS ALWAYS IN THE HOUSE. AND IN SUCH A CONSPICUOUS PLACE...

NEITHER WE NOR THE POLICE COULD FIND THE BODY...

WH-WHO...

WHO ARE YOU!?

WHAT!?

...THIS OLDER BROTHER OF YOURS!!

THUD

I'M A DETECTIVE!!

I'M CONAN EDOGAWA!

CALL THE POLICE RIGHT AWAY!!

POLICE!

P-P--

THEN YOU DRESSED HIM IN A BATHROBE AND SAT HIM DOWN ON A CHAIR IN THIS UPSTAIRS ROOM.

YOU WASHED THE BLOOD OFF HIM IN THE BATHROOM.

WHEN WE DISCOVERED THE BODY, YOU KNEW YOU HAD TO HURRY AND HIDE IT BEFORE THE POLICE ARRIVED.

YOU DEVISED A CLEVER TRICK, DIDN'T YOU?

WHEN WE CAME LOOKING FOR THE BODY WITH THE POLICE, YOU WERE PREPARED TO MEET US!

YOU TWO LOOKED ALIKE TO BEGIN WITH. SURE, YOU MIGHT NOT HAVE BEEN ABLE TO FOOL FAMILY, BUT THE SIMPLE DISGUISE WORKED WELL ENOUGH FOR PEOPLE WHO DIDN'T KNOW YOU!

YOU PUT ON A BATHROBE TOO, AND BOLDLY DISGUISED YOURSELF AS YOUR MURDERED OLDER BROTHER!!

THERE'S AN EMBANKMENT ON THE OTHER SIDE OF THE FENCE, BUT THERE'S A LEDGE WIDE ENOUGH FOR ONE PERSON.

WHILE THE POLICE WERE LOOKING FOR THE BODY, YOU WENT OUT THE UPSTAIRS WINDOW AND USED THE TREE TO GET OVER THE FENCE!

YOU PRETENDED TO BE UPSET AND EXCUSED YOURSELF UPSTAIRS.

...

ONCE OUTSIDE, YOU REMOVED YOUR DISGUISE AND CAME BACK AS YOURSELF TO THE FRONT DOOR!!

AND ANYWAY, DON'T YOU REMEMBER HOW HE YELLED AT YOU WHEN YOU BROKE THAT VASE!?

THE YOUNGER BROTHER WAS BY MY SIDE WHEN THAT HAPPENED!!

THAT'S ABSURD. THAT MAN WAS ALIVE! HE TURNED THE TV OFF WHEN HIS BROTHER TOLD HIM TO.

YEAH! THE YOUNGER BROTHER WAS THE MURDERER AND THE OLDER BROTHER SLEEPING UPSTAIRS WAS ACTUALLY THE DEAD MAN!!

OH. IT'S JUST YOU KIDS AGAIN.

THE POLICE STATION

WHAT? YOU FOUND THE BODY!?

YOU WAITED FOR THE RIGHT MOMENT TO SET OFF THE RECORDED VOICE GREETING ON YOUR ANSWERING MACHINE WITH THE SPEED-DIAL ON YOUR PHONE.

KRASH

BEEP

THAT ANGRY SHOUT WAS SOMETHING YOU RECORDED ON THE ANSWERING MACHINE BEFORE THE POLICE ARRIVED.

YOU USED THE VCR AND ANSWERING MACHINE IN THIS ROOM AND THE CELL PHONE HIDDEN IN YOUR SUIT.

YES. YOU STAGED IT TO MAKE IT APPEAR AS IF YOUR BROTHER WERE STILL ALIVE.

YOU MADE US THINK YOUR BROTHER WAS YELLING FROM UPSTAIRS!!

KEEP IT DOWN!!

AND OF COURSE, YOU HAD TURNED OFF THE RINGERS ON THE PHONES IN THE HOUSE.

JUST LIKE THIS...

BEEP

IF YOU HADN'T TAKEN THE CALL, THE ANSWERING MACHINE WOULD HAVE KICKED IN, BROADCASTING YOUR SHOUT AGAIN.

YOU PROBABLY SAW THE CALL LIGHT FLASHING WHEN THE CALL CAME.

KCHAK

I SAW PROOF OF THAT WHEN YOU GOT THAT WRONG NUMBER CALL. YOU PICKED UP THE PHONE EVEN THOUGH IT NEVER RANG.

MR. TOMOFUMI TANAKA...?

ISN'T THAT RIGHT?

AND THE TIME HE TURNED OFF THE TV-- YOU STAGED IT BY SETTING THE VCR TIMER AND TIMING YOUR ACTIONS ACCORDINGLY.

WHAT'S ALL THAT NOISE!? KEEP IT DOWN!!

BEEEP

BLIP BIP BOOP BIP BIP BEEP BOOP

142

"TEN" THE KANJI CHARACTER FOR "HEAVEN" HAS JUST BEEN LIT ON THE MOUNTAIN!!

WHAT A GRAND SIGHT!!

SAITAMA OKEYAMA HOTEL

OKEYAMA

TOSS

CHUCK

SAITAMA'S TENKAICHI FESTIVAL HAS FINALLY STARTED!!

TONIGHT?

I HOPE YOU HAVEN'T FORGOTTEN ABOUT TONIGHT.

I CAN'T EVEN ENJOY A NICE QUIET BATH.

REALLY! JUST WHEN I THOUGHT YOU'D LEFT FOR THE FESTIVAL, YOU COME BACK TO GET YOUR WALLET!

SORRY...

RATTLE

RATTLE

HEY! CAN'T YOU LOOK FOR IT MORE QUIETLY?

BRUSH BRUSH

YOU SAID YOU'D CELEBRATE WITH ME. THAT'S WHY I WENT TO THE TROUBLE OF COM--

BRUSH BRUSH

AND THIS MESS...!

WHAT'S GOING ON!?

WH-WHAT ARE YOU DOING DRESSED LIKE THAT?

!?

CLICK

I'M SORRY, BUT FORGET ABOUT TONIGHT.

BANG

BECAUSE THE GUEST OF HONOR...

WANT TO KNOW WHY?

WHAT!?

HEH
HEH
HEH

RUSTLE

...IS
DEAD.

THWUNK

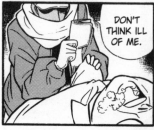

DON'T
THINK ILL
OF ME.

H-HEY
YOU
...!

DASH

UM...
DID YOU
JUST HEAR
SOMETHING
LIKE A
GUNSHOT
?

SHFF
SHFF

PTNK

204

DASH

KMP

KMP

KMP

FLICK

HEY, IT'S LIT! IT'S LIT!

*TEN-KA-ICHI, OR HEAVEN-UNDER-ONE, MEANS UNRIVALED.

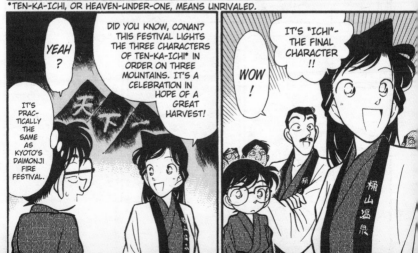

YEAH?

DID YOU KNOW, CONAN? THIS FESTIVAL LIGHTS THE THREE CHARACTERS OF TEN-KA-ICHI* IN ORDER ON THREE MOUNTAINS. IT'S A CELEBRATION IN HOPE OF A GREAT HARVEST!

IT'S PRACTICALLY THE SAME AS KYOTO'S DAIMONJI FIRE FESTIVAL.

IT'S "ICHI"- THE FINAL CHARACTER!!

WOW!

I'M GETTING TIRED OF BEING TREATED LIKE A LITTLE KID.

LIBERATE ME FROM BUNNY BONDAGE!

YEAH! DON'T YOU AGREE, CONAN?

IT'S QUITE PLEASANT TO STAY AT AN INN AND ENJOY A FESTIVAL ONCE IN A WHILE!

Y-YEAH.

HUF

HUF

HUF

PHEW. I MADE IT.

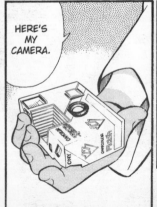

HERE'S MY CAMERA.

HOW ABOUT WITH THAT CHARACTER "ICHI" IN THE BACK-GROUND?

OH, SURE!

EXCUSE ME. COULD YOU TAKE MY PICTURE?

THANK YOU SO MUCH.

SNAP

WOW! YOU'RE A WRITER!!

THE PHOTOS ARE FOR MY RESEARCH.

I'M WORKING ON A TRAVELOGUE ON REGIONAL FESTIVALS.

REALLY? ARE YOU SURE?

IT'S A BOOK I WROTE.

IF YOU'RE INTERESTED, PLEASE TAKE THIS.

NO, NO. THIS TAN IS FROM DOING RESEARCH! I GO OVERSEAS A LOT FOR MY WORK.

YOU LOOK SO TAN, I THOUGHT YOU WERE AN ATHLETE OR SOMETHING.

I USED TO WRITE NOVELS A LONG TIME AGO UNDER THE PSEUDONYM "TOMOKAZU IMAI."

THE NAME'S NOT RINGING A BELL?

NORIKAZU SASAI ...?

Traveling Through Australia
Norikazu Sasai

OH, SATORU AND I GO WAY BACK. WE USED TO WRITE TOGETHER BACK IN THE DAY.

THAT'S WEIRD. SATORU IMATAKE, THE RECENT WINNER OF THE NAOMOTO AWARD, USED THAT SAME PEN NAME WHEN HE MADE HIS DEBUT.

BACK IN JUNIOR HIGH I USED TO READ BOOKS LIKE "ROMANCE UNDER THE MOON" AND "I CAN HEAR THE WIND" ALL THE TIME!!

OH, TOMOKAZU IMAI!? I KNOW THAT NAME!!

I THOUGHT WE COULD CELEBRATE HIS WINNING THE NAOMOTO AWARD WITH A NIGHT OF DRINKING RIGHT HERE IN HIS HOMETOWN.

YES... IN FACT, HE AND I CAME OUT TO THIS AREA TOGETHER TODAY.

WOW! YOU WROTE WITH THAT FAMOUS SATORU IMATAKE!?

TAKE OFF THAT COAT IF YOU'RE HOT.

PHEW. IT'S HOT.

'COURSE, I'M HERE FOR MY RESEARCH AS WELL.

SNAP

SNAP

OH... NO PROBLEM.

WOULD YOU MIND TAKING TWO OR THREE MORE?

YOU KNOW, THIS AREA IS GREAT.

MR. NORIKAZU SASAI?

HUH?

HUH?

I HAVE A FEW QUESTIONS ABOUT MR. SATORU IMATAKE.

I'M YOKOMIZO FROM THE SAITAMA POLICE!!

IT HAPPENED RIGHT IN THE HOTEL ROOM WHERE YOU TWO ARE STAYING.

HE WAS MURDERED!!

UM. DID SOMETHING HAPPEN TO IMATAKE?

HAVE WE MET? YOU LOOK FAMILIAR.

MM?

P-POLICE...?

WHAT!?

OKEYAMA HOTEL

THE VICTIM IS NOVELIST SATORU IMATAKE.

THE SUSPECT IS A YOUNG MAN WHO RAN FROM THE ROOM RIGHT AFTER THAT TIME.

GUESTS IN NEARBY ROOMS HEARD THE GUNSHOT. ACCORDING TO THEIR STATEMENTS, THE CRIME OCCURRED TWO OR THREE MINUTES AFTER 8 P.M.

THE MURDER WEAPON WAS A GUN.

A DETECTIVE...?

JUST A DETECTIVE.

H-HEY, WHO ARE YOU!?

HMM. A REMARKABLY CLEAN SHOT THROUGH THE HEAD.

YES. IT WAS RIGHT AROUND THE TIME THEY SHOWED THE TENKAICHI SPRING FESTIVAL ON TV.

YOU'RE SURE ABOUT THAT, RIGHT?

BY ANY CHANCE...

ARE YOU THE FAMOUS DETECTIVE RICHARD MOORE!?

Y-YES...

WOW! YOU'VE SOLVED SO MANY TOUGH CASES!! I ALWAYS READ ABOUT THEM IN THE PAPER!!

I'M THE ONE WHO SOLVED EVERY SINGLE ONE OF THEM.

RUSTLE RUSTLE

...

PLEASE! EXAMINE ANYTHING YOU'D LIKE. I'D APPRECIATE YOUR INPUT ON THE INVESTIGATION!!

WHAT IS IT?

FWP

HMM... THERE'S SOMETHING ON HIS MOUTH.

HUH
?

TOOTH-
PASTE.

TH-
THIS
IS...

D-DID YOU FIND ANYTHING, DETECTIVE MOORE?

IMPOSSIBLE KID! ALWAYS GETTING IN MY WAY.

OWW !

THE PERPE-TRATOR WAS AFTER THE VALU-ABLES.

THE VICTIM'S WALLET IS MISSING AND THE ROOM HAS BEEN RANSACKED.

A BUR-GLARY ?

I SEE STRONG INDICATIONS THAT IT WAS A BURGLARY.

PERHAPS IT WAS MADE TO LOOK LIKE A BURGLARY.

B-BUT, DETECTIVE MOORE, COULDN'T THERE BE ANOTHER POSSIBILITY?

THE VICTIM IS LYING NEAR THE DOOR. FROM THAT I DEDUCE THAT THE SUSPECT KNOCKED ON THE DOOR...

...AND WHEN THE VICTIM CARELESSLY OPENED IT, HE WAS IMMEDIATELY SHOT.

WHAT!?

MAYBE MR. SASAI MURDERED HIM. AFTER ALL, HE WAS STAYING IN THE SAME ROOM AS THE VICTIM.

I HAVE AN ALIBI!

IT WAS AROUND EIGHT WHEN THEY HEARD THE GUNSHOT AND SAW THAT MAN RUNNING OUT, RIGHT?

FROM EIGHT ON...

DON'T BE RIDICULOUS!!

THEY ONLY SAW HOW THE SUSPECT WAS DRESSED. NOBODY ACTUALLY SAW HIS FACE!!

BUT EYEWITNESSES SAY THE MURDERER WAS A YOUNG MAN.

BUT WASN'T IT TOWARDS THE END OF THE FESTIVAL THAT WE MET YOU?

YEAH...

ISN'T THAT RIGHT!?

THAT'S WHERE I MET MR. MOORE!

WHAT!?

...I WAS AT THE TENKAICHI SPRING FESTIVAL.

YES SIR!!

ALL RIGHT. GET THIS DEVELOPED RIGHT AWAY!!

YOU'LL SEE PROOF OF MY ALIBI!!

I'M TELLING YOU I WAS THERE FROM THE BEGINNING!! IF YOU THINK I'M LYING, JUST DEVELOP THE FILM IN HERE!!

DARN IT.

GLANCE

GLANCE

HEY, KID. DON'T TOUCH THAT!!

THAT'S WEIRD. IT'S GOT TO BE HERE.

WHAT ARE YOU UP TO, CONAN? GET OFF THE COUNTER.

UM... NOTHING.

HEY...

RUSTLE

RUSTLE

NEAR THE BODY...?

MM? ON THE CARPET NEAR THE BODY.

WHERE WAS THAT TOOTH-BRUSH?

THE VICTIM KNEW THE MURDERER.

I KNEW IT. DETECTIVE YOKOMIZO IS RIGHT. THIS WAS NO BURGLARY.

YEAH. IT WAS WORSE WHEN WE FIRST ARRIVED.

UM... WAS THE ROOM THIS MESSED UP WHEN YOU GUYS GOT HERE?

BUT WHY DOES HE HAVE SUCH A CONFIDENT SMILE?

I'M PRETTY SURE IT'S THIS MAN!

JUST WHAT KIND OF ALIBI CAN IT PROVIDE?

WHAT'S IN THAT FILM?

THEN LET'S TAKE A LOOK.

OH, GOOD!

DETECTIVE YOKOMIZO! THE PHOTOS ARE DEVELOPED!!

ONE HOUR LATER...

HOTEL

SEVEN PHOTOS IN ALL.

SEE? HERE'S CONAN'S BALLOON.

I TOOK THIS PHOTO!

HEY!

BUT HOW DO THESE SERVE AS AN ALIBI?

!?

THE CRIME TOOK PLACE AT 8:02. I THINK A FAST DRIVER COULD GET TO THE FESTIVAL FROM THIS HOTEL IN 40 MINUTES.

BUT "ICHI" WAS LIT SOMETIME AFTER 8:40 P.M.

THAT'S RIGHT! WE MET MR. SASAI RIGHT WHEN THE CHARACTER "ICHI" WAS LIT ON THE MOUNTAIN!

IT'S IMPOSSIBLE TO GET TO THE FESTIVAL FROM HERE IN 25 MINUTES, ISN'T IT?

THAT MEANS THEY EACH BURN FOR 25 MINUTES, AT MOST.

EACH CHARACTER BURNS OUT ABOUT TWO TO THREE MINUTES AFTER THE FOLLOWING ONE IS LIT.

DETECTIVE YOKOMIZO, THOSE CHARACTERS ARE LIT IN 20 MINUTE INTERVALS ON THREE MOUNTAINS. APPROXIMATELY HOW LONG DOES EACH ONE BURN?

IN OTHER WORDS, THIS PHOTO PROVES THAT HE WAS AT THE FESTIVAL BEFORE 8:25!!

THIS "TEN" SHOULD DISAPPEAR 25 MINUTES AFTER THE 8PM START OF THE FESTIVAL!!

TAKE A LOOK AT THE CHARACTER IN THE BACKGROUND OF THIS PHOTO!!

WHAT'S GOING ON!?

...

OF COURSE.

YOUR ALIBI IS PERFECT!

MAYBE THIS ALIBI IS A TRICK!?

BUT THE CIRCUMSTANCES SUGGEST OTHERWISE.

WAS THE CRIME COMMITTED BY A STRANGER, AFTER ALL...?

# FILE 10:
# THE PERFECT ALIBI!?

SAITAMA OKEYAMA HOTEL

WELL
...

...

OF COURSE.

YOUR ALIBI IS PERFECT, MR. SASAI!

Y-YES ...?

LISTEN, DETECTIVE YOKOMIZO.

NOW, NOW ...

HAVEN'T I BEEN TELLING YOU? I HAVE AN ALIBI!!

*HMPH.* YOU'RE SO STUBBORN.

NO DISRESPECT, DETECTIVE MOORE, BUT I STILL CAN'T HELP BUT THINK HE'S OUR MAN.

AND IN FACT, WE OURSELVES MET HIM AT THE FESTIVAL AND RACHEL TOOK A FEW PHOTOS OF HIM.

HOWEVER, MR. SASAI STATES THAT HE WAS ALREADY AT THE TENKAICHI SPRING FESTIVAL BY EIGHT.

GUESTS IN NEARBY ROOMS HEARD THE GUNSHOT. RIGHT AFTERWARD, THEY WITNESSED A SUSPICIOUS MAN RUNNING FROM THIS ROOM.

SOMEBODY SHOT THE NOVELIST MR. SATORU IMATAKE IN THIS ROOM AROUND 8:02 OR 8:03.

TRUE. IT WOULD'VE BEEN POSSIBLE TO GET FROM THE HOTEL TO THE FESTIVAL BY THEN IF YOU DROVE FAST.

BUT YOU MET HIM AROUND 8:40.

LOOK!! IN THE BACKGROUND OF THIS PHOTO YOU CAN SEE THE CHARACTER FOR "TEN." IT WAS LIT AT EIGHT WHEN THE FESTIVAL BEGAN AND IT BURNED OUT 25 MINUTES LATER.

BUT NOT EVERY PHOTO WAS TAKEN *AFTER* HE MET US.

B-BUT...

IT'S IMPOSSIBLE TO GET TO THE FESTIVAL FROM THE HOTEL IN 25 MINUTES. IN OTHER WORDS IT'S IMPOSSIBLE FOR HIM TO HAVE COMMITTED THE CRIME!!

IN OTHER WORDS, THIS PHOTO PROVES THAT MR. SASAI WAS AT THE FESTIVAL SOMETIME BEFORE 8:25!!

BESIDES, THAT WAS A DISPOSABLE CAMERA! HOW COULD I HAVE DONE SOMETHING LIKE THAT?

HA HA HA... I HANDED THE CAMERA DIRECTLY TO YOU COPS FOR DEVELOPMENT.

THERE COULD HAVE BEEN AN OVER EXPOSURE OR SOMETHING. SOMEONE KNOWLEDGEABLE ABOUT CAMERAS MIGHT--

IS THERE A POSSIBILITY THAT THE PHOTO WAS ALTERED?

SIR! THERE WERE NO SIGNS OF THE CAMERA OR THE FILM BEING TAMPERED!

YOU'RE THE ONE WHO DEVELOPED THE PHOTOS, RIGHT?

IT'S NOT FAIR TO BE SO SUSPICIOUS OF MR. SASAI JUST BECAUSE HE'S AN OLD FRIEND OF THE VICTIM AND HE HAPPENED TO BE STAYING IN THE SAME ROOM.

NOW, NOW, DETECTIVE YOKOMIZO.

...

WHAT DID I TELL YOU!

THEY SAID MR. SASAI LEFT THE HOTEL AROUND 7:30 TO GO TO THE FESTIVAL.

OH THAT? I ASKED AT THE FRONT DESK.

YOU CAME DIRECTLY TO THE FESTIVAL TO FIND HIM, DIDN'T YOU?

HUH?

BUT LISTEN, HOW DID YOU KNOW HE WAS AT THE FESTIVAL?

164

AS YOU CAN SEE, I FORGOT MY WATCH TODAY.

I KEPT CHECKING ON THE TIME BECAUSE I WANTED TO MAKE SURE I COULD SEE THE CHARACTER "TEN" BEFORE IT BURNED OUT AROUND 8:20!!

YES. THE PEOPLE AT THE FRONT DESK WERE QUITE CERTAIN ABOUT THAT BECAUSE HE'D REPEATEDLY ASKED THEM WHAT TIME IT WAS.

HMPH.

HMM. YOU EVEN KNOW THE TIME?

IMATAKE'S DEAD, HIS WALLET IS MISSING AND THE ROOM HAS BEEN TURNED UPSIDE DOWN. NO MATTER HOW YOU LOOK AT IT, IT'S THE WORK OF A THIEF.

DID YOU FORGET ABOUT THE SCENE HERE?

THAT'S ENOUGH OF THAT!

THAT BUGS ME. IT'S AS IF YOU WERE INTENTIONALLY CREATING AN ALIBI.

...

I WISH YOU'D HURRY UP AND GET TO WORK FINDING THE MAN WHO MURDERED MY FRIEND!

JUDGING FROM THE FACT THAT THE BODY WAS NEAR THE FRONT DOOR...

...WE ALREADY DETERMINED WHAT HAPPENED. THE CULPRIT KNOCKED ON THE DOOR. WHEN IMATAKE FOOLISHLY OPENED IT, HE WAS SHOT.

HEY. AREN'T YOU WORRIED, SIR?

MAYBE THE ROBBER STOLE SOMETHING FROM YOUR STUFF, TOO!

YOU'RE STAYING IN THIS ROOM, RIGHT?

YOU'VE BEEN BUSY TALKING TO THE POLICE THE WHOLE TIME YOU'VE BEEN HERE.

HUH?

SHOULDN'T YOU BE CHECKING THINGS OUT?

OR DO YOU KNOW THAT NOTHING OF YOURS WAS STOLEN?

IT'S NOT LIKE YOU RANSACKED THE ROOM YOURSELF ...!

YOU COULDN'T KNOW THAT, COULD YOU?

!?

I'LL GO CHECK RIGHT NOW.

WHAT WITH THE DEATH OF MY FRIEND AND ALL, I DIDN'T EVEN THINK OF IT.

HA HA HA... RIGHT YOU ARE, MY BOY.

WATCH IT, CONAN.

HUH?

M-MR. IMATAKE...

WHO ARE YOU?

MR. IMATAKE!!

MR. IMATAKE!!

...NOT THAT I BROUGHT ANY VALUABLES.

NOTHING WAS STOLEN FROM MY LUGGAGE...

OH, YOU MEAN THAT SAGA THAT STARTED A YEAR AGO?

THE *LITERARY ARTS MONTHLY* IS THE MAGAZINE RUNNING "BRAVE SWORD LEGEND" BY IMATAKE!!

I CAN'T BELIEVE IT.

THE POLICE CONTACTED OUR OFFICE SO I RUSHED STRAIGHT HERE!!

I'M YAMADA WITH THE *LITERARY ARTS MONTHLY*. I'M MR. IMATAKE'S EDITOR!!

WHO WOULD'VE THOUGHT SOMETHING LIKE THIS COULD HAPPEN!?

OH, I JUST CAME HERE TO CELEBRATE IMATAKE'S NAOMOTO AWARD. I DRAGGED HIM HERE TO SAITAMA SO WE COULD LIVE IT UP AND DRINK THE NIGHT AWAY.

WHY ARE YOU HERE?

YES ...

A-ARE YOU BY ANY CHANCE MR. SASAI!?

...

WH-WHAT A FIX! IT'S TOO LATE TO ASK ANOTHER WRITER, AND I'D NEVER BE ABLE TO FIND A WORK THAT COULD COMPARE TO MR. IMATAKE'S.

OH YEAH!! MR. IMATAKE'S DEADLINE IS TOMOR-ROW!!

COME TO THINK OF IT, IMATAKE MENTIONED THAT HIS DEADLINE WAS APPROACHING BUT THAT HE HADN'T WRITTEN ANYTHING YET.

HUH?

RUSTLE RUSTLE

OH WELL ...

!?

IF YOU'D LIKE, YOU CAN USE THIS.

WHAT IS THIS?

IT'S A PIECE I WROTE SOME TIME AGO.

IMATAKE HAS BEEN BADGERING ME TO SHOW IT TO HIM SO I JUST HAPPENED TO BRING IT TODAY.

BESIDES, WHEN WE WERE DECIDING ON THE MAIN SERIAL FOR THE *LITERARY ART MONTHLY*, YOUR NAME WAS MENTIONED AS A CANDIDATE.

SINCE IT'S BY SOMEONE WHO USED TO WRITE COLLABORATIVELY WITH MR. IMATAKE, EVERYBODY IN EDITORIAL IS BOUND TO AGREE!!

I DON'T THINK IT CAN COMPARE TO IMATAKE'S NOVEL, BUT...

PLEASE, I BEG YOU.

MM, I DON'T KNOW. I HAVE OTHER PROJECTS...

I-IF YOU WOULDN'T MIND, YOU COULD KEEP WRITING FOR *LITERARY ART MONTHLY*.

BUT ARE YOU SURE? THIS IS JUST A PROLOGUE OF A LONG PIECE!

WELL, I HAVE TO TAKE THIS SCRIPT TO THE OFFICE.

TH-THANK YOU VERY MUCH!!

ALL RIGHT. I'LL WRITE FOR THE SAKE OF MY LATE FRIEND, IMATAKE!!

ISN'T IT HIGH TIME YOU LET ME GO?

HEY, DETECTIVE.

...FOR THE SAKE OF POOR IMATAKE, KILLED BY SOME IDIOT THIEF.

LOOKS LIKE I HAVE TO HURRY HOME AND GET WORKING...

YOU HEARD THE CONVERSATION.

WELL... HE WAS RATHER NEAT. HE ALWAYS SHAVED BEFORE LEAVING THE HOUSE.

WHAT WAS HE LIKE? WAS HE CLEAN? SLOPPY?

THEN... YOU KNOW HIS PERSONALITY AND STUFF TOO, RIGHT?

NOT THE KID AGAIN.

Y-YEAH...

HEY MISTER!! YOU JUST SAID YOU AND MR. IMATAKE WERE OLD FRIENDS, RIGHT?

WON'T YOU TELL ME SECRETLY?

WHAT'S WEIRD?

HEY! WAIT, KID!!

I'M GONNA GO REPORT IT TO THE POLICE!

HUH?

THAT'S WEIRD. THAT CAN'T BE.

HE LIKED TO BE NEAT, OKAY!?

HA HA HA... SO HE BRUSHED HE TEETH! EVERYONE DOES THAT!

Y-YEAH...?

BUT I THOUGHT HE WAS SHOT THE MOMENT HE OPENED THE DOOR.

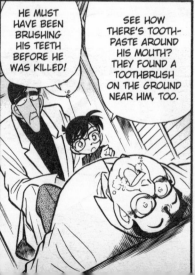

HE MUST HAVE BEEN BRUSHING HIS TEETH BEFORE HE WAS KILLED!

SEE HOW THERE'S TOOTHPASTE AROUND HIS MOUTH? THEY FOUND A TOOTHBRUSH ON THE GROUND NEAR HIM, TOO.

DO THEY?

PEOPLE DON'T USUALLY GREET STRANGERS AT THE DOOR WITH A TOOTH-BRUSH IN HAND AND TOOTHPASTE IN THEIR MOUTH.

TH-THE BOY IS EXACTLY RIGHT.

WHAT!?

!?

THAT MEANS THAT THE PERSON WHO CAME TO VISIT WAS SOMEONE THE VICTIM KNEW AND WAS EXPECTING.

IF SOME-BODY PAID AN UNEXPECTED VISIT, HE WOULDN'T HAVE COME TO THE DOOR LOOKING THE WAY HE DID!

EITHER THAT, OR ...

172

WHAT ?

IN EITHER CASE, YOU FIT THE DESCRIPTION, MR. SASAI.

...THE MURDERER WAS ALREADY IN THE ROOM.

WHO CARES IF IMATAKE WAS BRUSHING HIS TEETH OR NOT!!?

DON'T BE RIDICULOUS !!!

IF YOU INSIST ON ACCUSING ME OF THE MURDER, THEN PROVE IT!!

I HAVE THIS PHOTO !!

FWAP

BECAUSE I WAS REALLY AT THE FESTIVAL FROM THE BEGINNING !!

NO! YOU CAN'T !!

CAN YOU PROVE THAT I'M THE MURDERER !?

AND HE KILLED MR. IMATAKE.

HE RANSACKED THE ROOM TO MAKE IT LOOK LIKE A BURGLARY.

THIS MAN IS THE MURDERER !!

THERE'S NO DOUBT.

HE HAD PLENTY OF TIME TO MAKE IT THERE AFTER COMMITTING THE CRIME AT THE HOTEL!

WE MET HIM AT THE FESTIVAL AT 8:40.

THE CIRCUM-STANTIAL EVIDENCE AND HIS BEHAVIOR SAY THAT LOUD AND CLEAR.

HE DID IT.

WHY WOULD SOMEBODY WHO CLAIMS HE WAS AT THE FESTIVAL FROM THE BEGINNING SAY SOMETHING LIKE THAT AT 8:40!?

*PHEW.* I MADE IT.

AND WHEN WE MET HIM AT THE FESTIVAL, THE FIRST WORDS OUT OF HIS MOUTH WERE ODD.

174

IT SHOWS HIM AT THE FESTIVAL PRIOR TO 8:25.

HE HAS A PERFECT ALIBI!!!

BUT HE HAS THAT PHOTO!!

NEITHER THE CAMERA NOR THE FILM HAVE BEEN TAMPERED WITH.

BUT HOW?

HOW DID HE GET THAT PHOTO?

SOME CLUE TO BREAK DOWN HIS ALIBI!

DARN IT! THERE HAS TO BE SOMETHING...

PHOTOS TAKEN AFTER 8:40 DO NOTHING FOR HIS ALIBI.

BESIDES, HE WENT OUT OF HIS WAY TO GET HIS PICTURE TAKEN BY RACHEL EVEN AFTER THE ALIBI PHOTO.

I NEED ANOTHER CLUE!!

THINK! I'VE GOT TO THINK BACK TO THE FIRST MOMENT WE MET HIM!

!?

HEY, STOP !!

SORRY, BUT I'M OUT OF HERE!

WHAT WAS THAT ABOUT !?

TAKE OFF THAT COAT IF YOU'RE HOT.

PHEW. IT'S HOT.

THAT'S RIGHT! IN THE MIDDLE OF THE FESTIVAL ...

HOW ABOUT WITH THAT CHARACTER "ICHI" IN THE BACK-GROUND?

COME TO THINK OF IT, WHEN HE ASKED RACHEL TO TAKE HIS PICTURE ...

I COULD'VE SWORN ...

MAYBE HE COULDN'T TAKE IT OFF?

WHY DIDN'T HE TAKE IT OFF?

BUT WHY ?

HERE'S MY CAMERA.

!?

I'LL SUE YOU IF YOU DON'T STOP!!

FWP FWP FWP

THAT'S ENOUGH. DAMN IT!!

WAIT A MINUTE!! I'M NOT FINISHED WITH YOU YET.

GRAB

THAT'S WHAT IT WAS.

I SEE ...

THAT MAN DID IT, ALL RIGHT.

AND WHAT'S MORE ...

I FIGURED OUT THE TRICK !!

... THIS MURDER WAS PREMEDITATED !!!

TO BE CONTINUED IN CASE CLOSED VOLUME 7!

From Rumiko Takahashi, the princess of manga and the creator of Inuyasha and Ranma, *Maison Ikkoku* is a love story that takes place in Japan, but could take place anywhere.

Funny, touching, and a tad off-kilter, MAISON IKKOKU is the great Rumiko Takahashi at her very best.

GOLLANCZ MANGA

# find out more at www.orionbooks.co.uk

# maison ikkoku

## THE UNMISSABLE NEW
## GOLLANCZ MANGA SERIES STARTS HERE!

Yusaku's attempts to study get off to a bad start when he falls head-over-heels for the new manager, and he's a long, long way from winning her heart. For Kyoko already has somebody else on her mind . . . a mysterious "Mr. Soichiro" . . .

# FLAME OF RECCA ™

Story and Art by
**Nobuyuki Anzai**    Vol.**1**

## COME ON BABY, LIGHT MY FIRE

Recca Hanabishi's a high-school kid who hopes to become a ninja,
whose life is unexpectedly turned upside down by a cute and
mysterious girl named Yanagi. Suddenly Recca finds he's had super
ninja secret powers all along, but can Recca learn to use them,
or his new ability to control fire . . .

    FLAME OF RECCA © 1995 by Nobuyuki ANZAI/Shogakukan Inc

Charged with finding seven Celestial Warrior protectors, and given a mission to save her new world, Miaka encounters base villains and dashing heroes — and still manages to worry about where her next banquet is coming from.

**VOLUMES 1-6 OUT NOW!**

GOLLANCZ MANGA

# find out more at www.orionbooks.co.uk

# fushigi yûgi ™

Welcome to the wonderfully exciting, funny, and heartfelt tale of Miaka Yûki, a normal high-school girl who is suddenly whisked away into a fictional version of ancient China.

Spooky crimes, baffling robberies, and comic would-be detectives, no crime's too tough to crack for Jimmy!

. . . especially not his personal case: to find the mysterious masked men and make them change him back . . .

All the clues are here – can you solve the case before Jimmy does?

**VOLUMES 1-6 OUT NOW!**

**find out more at www.orionbooks.co.uk**

# CASE CLOSED ™

**MEET JIMMY KUDO.**

Ace high-school student with keen powers of observation, he helps police solve the baffling crimes . . . until, hot on the trial of a suspect, he's accosted and fed a strange chemical which transforms him into a puny grade schooler!

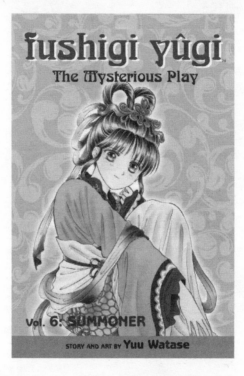

# COMING IN JANUARY FROM GOLLANCZ MANGA

Story and art by
**Gosho Aoyama**

Vol. 7

名探偵コナン

GOLLANCZ MANGA

Conan Edogawa, ace detective has a new case to solve — and a dead pianist as his client. Spooky cursed piano, or fiendish crime — can you solve the case before Conan does?

## find out more at www.orionbooks.co.uk

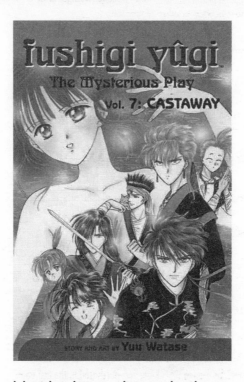

# COMPLETE OUR SURVEY AND
# LET US KNOW WHAT YOU THINK!

❏ Please do NOT send me information about Gollancz Manga, or other Orion titles, products, news and events, special offers or other information.

Name: _____

Address: _____

Town: _____ County: _____ Postcode: _____

❏ Male ❏ Female    Date of Birth (dd/mm/yyyy): ___/___/_____
(under 13? Parental consent required)

## What race/ethnicity do you consider yourself? (please check one)

❏ Asian                    ❏ Black                    ❏ Hispanic

❏ White/Caucasian          ❏ Other: _____

## Which Gollancz Manga title did you purchase?

| Case Closed | Dragon Ball | Fushigi Yûgi | Yu-Gi-Oh! |
|---|---|---|---|
| ❏ 1 ❏ 2 ❏ 3 | ❏ 1 ❏ 2 ❏ 3 | ❏ 1 ❏ 2 ❏ 3 | ❏ 1 ❏ 2 ❏ 3 |
| ❏ 4 ❏ 5 ❏ 6 | ❏ 4 ❏ 5 ❏ 6 | ❏ 4 ❏ 5 ❏ 6 | ❏ 4 ❏ 5 ❏ 6 |

## What other Gollancz Manga do you own?

| Case Closed | Dragon Ball | Fushigi Yûgi | Yu-Gi-Oh! |
|---|---|---|---|
| ❏ 1 ❏ 2 ❏ 3 | ❏ 1 ❏ 2 ❏ 3 | ❏ 1 ❏ 2 ❏ 3 | ❏ 1 ❏ 2 ❏ 3 |
| ❏ 4 ❏ 5 ❏ 6 | ❏ 4 ❏ 5 ❏ 6 | ❏ 4 ❏ 5 ❏ 6 | ❏ 4 ❏ 5 ❏ 6 |

## How many anime and/or manga titles have you purchased in the last year?
## How many were Gollancz Manga titles?

| Anime | Manga | GM |
|---|---|---|
| ❏ None | ❏ None | ❏ None |
| ❏ 1-4 | ❏ 1-4 | ❏ 1-4 |
| ❏ 5-10 | ❏ 5-10 | ❏ 5-10 |
| ❏ 11+ | ❏ 11+ | ❏ 11+ |

**Reason for purchase:** (check all that apply)
- ❏ Special Offer
- ❏ Favou[...]
- ❏ In store promotion If so please indicate which [...]
- ❏ Recommendation
- ❏ Other[...]

C000241752

**Where did you make your purchase?**
- ❏ Bookshop
- ❏ Comic Shop
- ❏ Music Store
- ❏ Newsagent
- ❏ Video Game Store
- ❏ Supermarket
- ❏ Other: _____
- ❏ Online: _____

**What kind of manga would you like to read?**
- ❏ Adventure
- ❏ Comic Strip
- ❏ Fantasy
- ❏ Fighting
- ❏ Horror
- ❏ Mystery
- ❏ Romance
- ❏ Science Fiction
- ❏ Sports
- ❏ Other: _____

**Which do you prefer?**
- ❏ Sound effects in English
- ❏ Sound effects in Japanese with English captions
- ❏ Sound effects in Japanese only with a glossary at the back

**Want to find out more about Manga?**
Look it up at www.orionbooks.co.uk, or www.viz.com

**THANK YOU!**
Please send the completed form to:

**Manga Survey**
**Orion Books**
**Orion House**
**5 Upper St Martin's Lane**
**London, WC2H 9EA**

All information provided will be used for internal purposes only.
We promise not to sell or otherwise divulge your details.

NO PURCHASE NECESSARY. Requests not in compliance with all terms of this form will not be acknowledged or returned. All submissions are subject to verification and become property of Gollancz Manga.